Oct 3/2003

To Catharine

M E L B O R I N S M.D.

Keep travelling

+ smiling

Go Mel

GO
Away

JUST FOR THE
HEALTH OF IT

WHOLISTIC PRESS
TORONTO • DALLAS

published in conjunction with eastendbooks

Library of Congress Number: 00-109875

Canadian Cataloguing in Publication Data

Borins, Mel
    Go away just for the health of it

ISBN 0-9690565-1-6

1. Vacations - Psychological aspects. 2. Travel - Psychological aspects.
3. Vacations - Health aspects. 4. Borins, Mel - Journeys. 5. Voyages and travel. I. Title

G151.B67 2000   910'.01'9   C00-932599-9

Printed in Canada

ACKNOWLEDGEMENTS
"Grateful acknowledgement is made to the following for the use
of previously published material:"

2/6/81	Never Knock the Local Healer Medical Post
16/6/81	Have Some Faith — Come to Fiji to Get Healed Medical Post
7/81	Tahunga Knowhow is Passed Down Though Family Medical Post
11/81	Recalling the Horrors of Hiroshima Medical Post
12/81	Ancient Herbal Remedies Hit the Spot Medical Post
6/82	Snakes, Monkeys Used in Oriental Medicine Medical Post
12/89	Life is one continuous celebration in Bali Globe and Mail
1/90	Escape to Kashmir Doctor's Review
2/90	Coming of Age in Kashmir Medical Post
2/10/90	Bali-ho! Medical Post
30/4/91	Go to Goa before Goa gets gone! Medical Post
5/5/92	Afghanistan: I'll be back again Medical Post
9/2/93	Getting away from it all...again Medical Post
16/2/93	Cook Islands' messengers from heaven Medical Post
22/6/93	Algonquin Bound Medical Post
3011/93	Bali High:Spiritual Celebrations... Medical Post
7/12/93	Doctor breeds clean living in Japanese health-care garden Medical Post
17/ 5/94	Funeral burial rites of Torajan people.. shocking Medical Post
5/11/94	Traveller's Spirit of Giving Family Practice
2/6/96	The Multitudinous Masses of Beijing Medical Post
2/96	Holidays for Health Sake Leisureways
8/4/96	In the jungle the lions didn't sleep at night Family Practice.
31/8/96	Birds of a feather flock over to Algonquin Park Toronto Star
8/10/96	Suzhou:the Venice of China Medical Post
3/2/97	Worthwhile Trip off China's Main Roads Medical Post
18/2/97	Taiwan:Where West Meets East Medical Post
07/04/97	Sinking to New Depths Family Practice
21/7/97	Regroup Your Energies with a Travel Diary FamilyPractice
9/3/98	Trouble in Indonesia Family Practice
31/3/98	Orangutans-Meeting Sumatra's Men of the Forest Medical Post
5/98	Have Family Will Travel Family
15/6/98	Forget first class-here's no class Family Practice
18/9/2000	Are you a tourist or a traveller? Medical Post

Dedicated to Larry, David and Marc

My favorite traveling companions

"Travel is fatal to prejudice, bigotry and narrow-mindedness and many of our people need it sorely…Broad, wholesome, charitable views cannot be acquired by vegetating in one's little corner of the earth."

—Mark Twain

CONTENTS

PHOTO CREDITS

Cover photo: Mel at sunset over ricefields in Bali, Indonesia by Bonnie Borins

Page 112 Houseboat on Nagin Lake, Kashmir, India by Bonnie Borins

Page 224 Gujars, Phalgam, Kashmir, India by Bonnie Borins

Photos by MEL BORINS:

Page 109 Sunset, West Bali, Indonesia

Page 146 The King, Masai Mara Game Reserve, Kenya

Page 182 Rice Planting, Sulawesi, Indonesia

Page 196 Orangutan, Sumatra, Indonesia

Page 205 Dani Natives, Baliem Valley, Irian Jaya, Indonesia

Page 231 Bonnie in Bamyan, Afghanistan

Page 234 Guilin, China

Page 260 Highway 60, Algonquin Park, Canada

FOREWORD

At first glance "Go Away" may seem to be light reading. But as one reads the stories more carefully, the wisdom that is woven into each one of them becomes more apparent. In some cases the insights are simple and practical in nature, while in others the knowledge is more philosophical. Whatever the case, this book helps to enlighten, stimulate and inspire the reader.

On a personal level the book helped me question some important issues we all must deal with. How do we spend our life time and why do we need to "get away" from our lives? What is a vacation? Do we need to travel in order to get away or vacation?

Maybe all we need to do is stop answering the telephone. Dr. Borins' book has also helped me clarify many issues related to my life and life time. By reading this book I was able to discover what feels right for me to do that actually creates a vacation for me.

I personally do not want to sit in airports or on airplanes for endless hours going to some distant land. If they could beam me up, then I would be glad to go. I have realized that what seems appropriate for me may not be what feels true for someone else. I think Mel shares this in his life and journeys with his wife and family.

I encourage you to read and learn where to go with your life before your time runs out. When you accept your mortality you are more likely to "get away" from the things and people that you do not love. You are more apt to spend time with the people and things that do matter. This becomes a true vacation in every sense of the word. I think Mel and I as physicians understand this from our experience.

I admire Mel for his courage to step away from his office and live his authentic life's journey with his family's support. He is not living a role but a life. Most of us need to "get away" from the roles we play, in order to truly live.

Read on and learn how to begin your vacation and life.

Bernie Siegel M.D.
Author of *Love, Medicine and Miracles*
and *Prescriptions For Living*

Part One

INTRODUCTION

I'd like to infect you with a bug. No scientist can culture it; no doctor can cure it. Indeed, once this bug is in your system, it's there for life. It is the travel bug.

There is no doubt that holidays are healing. When you are on vacation the mind and the body start to repair themselves from the stress and strain of everyday life. Taking a holiday is very good for what ails you.

I've always joked that I should open a travel service as part of my medical practice. If you came to see me, I would take your full medical history, do a complete physical, order any necessary tests and then, depending on your symptoms, I would prescribe an appropriate vacation.

I would take into consideration your age, health, income, goals and personal needs. If you were out of shape, for example, a fitness spa or ski vacation might be indicated to build your strength, stimulate your heart and tighten up your muscles. If you were suffering from burnout, stretching out on an isolated island without television or telephones would be a step towards rejuvenation. If you were feeling spiritually drained then spending a few weeks in a yoga ashram, a Tibetan monastery or a religious retreat may help you to revive your spiritual connection and put you back on a new path.

Vacations can change the direction of your life and even

help you to recover from a physical or emotional illness. I don't have the cure for the "travel bug"; instead I'd like to spread it far and wide.

Many scientific studies support the idea that vacations are therapeutic. Research shows, for example, the lack of vacations may be contributing directly to heart disease. Nearly 750 women aged 45-64 were interviewed as part of a comprehensive study conducted in Framingham, Massachusetts from 1965 to 1985. During the first two years of the survey the women completed a questionnaire that asked them about everything from money to children, religion to vacations. At this time they were all free of heart disease. Over the next 20 years the level and severity of heart disease was measured. The researchers found that those women — regardless of race, age or occupation — who took fewer vacations had significantly more heart attacks. Homemakers, for example, who rarely took a vacation (less than once every six years) had almost twice the risk of developing heart problems or dying from heart disease as homemakers who took a vacation at least twice a year.

Other studies have also shown a healthy relationship between feeling good and getting away from it all. At the Veteran's Administrative Medical Center in Iowa City patients receiving dialysis were put on a schedule of mini-vacations. Hospital staff noted that patients who had previously appeared isolated or withdrawn perked up and took part in conversations after their vacation. Staff members also noted that patients were more helpful when it came to taking their medication and following their treatment plan. Carroll Roy and Esther Atcherson, two social workers involved in the study said that the mini-vacations appeared to "lift the aura of depression" that often goes hand in hand with a chronic illness. The benefits not only to patients but also to their families and hospital staff members could never be measured in dollars. Being able to take a holiday enhanced their emotional and social lives.

Community Involvement Through Travel is a service run through Community Living Mississauga, a city outside Toronto. For many years it has facilitated taking mentally challenged adults on vacations. The program lets participants plan their holidays and make their own decisions. These vacations have made a huge difference in helping to increase the happiness and joy in the lives of these people who normally would not be able to take a holiday.

Dr. James Sands from the South Coast Institute for Applied Gerontology, studied 112 women aged 65-92 in Atlanta. He found a strong relationship between more stressful life events and a decline in intellectual functioning. However, there was a positive relationship between taking vacations and increasing intellectual functioning.

Dr. Sharon Hymer, a professor at New York University, wrote an article entitled "An Alternative to the 'Traumatizing' Vacation: the Enriching, Expansive Vacation", which was published in the American Journal of Psychoanalysis. She believes that vacations can bring new insights to both the patient and the therapist involved in psychoanalysis. Dr Hymer maintains that taking time off can enrich the self, as well as our relationship to others. Traveling, it seems, gives us new and novel opportunities to discover aspects of ourselves that do not emerge at home. By "emptying" themselves of everyday concerns and anxieties she thought both the analyst and the patient would benefit.

Readers of Psychology Today completed more than 10,000 questionnaires. The survey found that, "Thirty-seven percent of those surveyed said they needed time off to rest, recharge their batteries and get renewed. Eighteen percent said their primary reason for a vacation was to learn. They go away to seek intellectual or spiritual enrichment, to investigate places they have never seen or to discover their roots. Others chose to go away for family togetherness, exotic adventure, self-discovery and escaping routines."

Finally, Kaiser analyzed the responses of 390 steel workers to an extended paid vacation lasting 13 weeks. He found that the vacations were strongly beneficial to family life. Workers reported more interactions and shared activities with their spouse and children. After returning to work, a full quarter of the respondents felt they were more efficient and that their jobs were more interesting.

The benefits of getting away from it all, it seems, extend well after we've gotten away from it all.

GETTING AWAY

The word "holiday" comes from the word holy, or god-like. It usually refers to a day of freedom from labour or a day set aside for rest and relaxation. "Vacation, " on the other hand, is derived from vacate and generally means leaving or getting away from the daily routine.

As soon as babies learn to crawl they set off to learn about their surroundings. They are curious. They want to touch things; they want to put things in their mouths. As adults we still have that innate sense of curiosity, although many of us feel safer when we stay close to home and don't wander very far.

Historically, however, people have always been wanderers in search of a better place to live. Tribes like the Aborigines of Australia still go on "walkabouts" and set off across the desert for a change of scenery. There is a little bit of the nomad in each one of us: we have an inherent desire to discover the world around us.

There are few undiscovered places left and it is difficult to find an isolated and untouched corner of the earth. But this does not mean that every journey we make isn't unique and exciting. A well-organized, one-week package holiday can have lasting benefits. Sometimes, of course, the trip away from home sparks an inward exploration.

TIME FOR A HOLIDAY

Since the industrial revolution there has been a steady decline in the number of hours we work and a steady increase in the amount of free time available to us. Science, machines and technology do much of the manual labour that at one time ate up so much of our day. Factories are now computerized, and there is less human sweat and toil. The use of computerized robots to do a person's job more efficiently, and more cheaply, is already a reality and probably the way of the future.

This has meant shorter working weeks, more lay-offs, and more unemployment. It also means more time for fun and frolicking. Filling our free time is a billion dollar industry in North America.

But for many of us leisure time can be difficult to handle. The strong work ethic we were raised with makes us feel lazy or guilty when we do not have our noses to the grindstone. This guilt has been reinforced by an educational system that is focused on helping students develop marketable skills so they can find a job. Our educational institutions have not made teaching us what to do with our free time a priority.

And we do have lots of free time. Indeed, it's now part of our lifestyle — and our work. Many corporations offer employees a paid sabbatical. Unpaid leaves of absence are already part of many union contracts enabling employees to take time off to pursue educational or personal interests knowing their jobs will be waiting for them when they return. Even young professionals are preparing their partnership agreements to include longer vacation times and regular sabbaticals. The right to annual vacations of a minimum duration is prescribed by law in 78 countries and some are so convinced of the necessity that there are penalties for deferring the vacation.

Therefore, it becomes exceedingly important to use your time away from work wisely: to recharge your batteries, to re-think your career options, to re-evaluate your goals in life, and to devote time and attention to your loved ones.

WHERE THERE'S A WILL

Many people argue that if they go away they will miss out on an opportunity at work. Some people fear that if they go away their job will be gone when they return. Others claim traveling is too expensive. In many ways, however, these fears are excuses. You don't have to be at work every day to be a valuable employee. Indeed, a refreshed employee is actually a more valuable — and productive — employee.

You also don't have to blow your life savings to enjoy a holiday. If you are low on cash, then you can travel cheaply. Take a bus and stay with relatives or friends. Or get creative. What places could you visit that don't require a lot of money? Government-run campgrounds, for example, offer you the whole outdoors for rock-bottom prices.

There are some people who wouldn't think twice about buying an expensive suit or dress for hundreds of dollars but wouldn't consider using that money for a vacation. Some people have thousands of dollars in the bank but won't take a few weeks off, unless it's for business. On the other hand, there are those individuals who scrimp and save so they can take their next holiday. They would rather travel than buy one more pair of designer jeans, gamble at the racetrack, or splurge on nouveau cuisine or expensive bottles of wine. What these people intuitively know is that getting away actually saves them money in the long run; it's a more cost-effective way to enhance a marriage, prevent job burn-out and deal with stress than taking pills or going for psychotherapy.

There is a serious inequality in vacationing. People on social assistance, the uneducated, those with very low income, and the disabled are less likely to be in a position to take a vacation. Someday there will be public policy in place based on Article 24 of the United Nations Declaration of Human Rights that affirms "everyone has the right to rest and leisure."

I'm sure you've heard the expression "where there's a will there's a way". Even if you are presently not in a position to travel or take a vacation, do not be bitter or think negatively about your future chances. I have known a young couple that couldn't afford to travel, but won a free trip to Colombia. I have friends who were given cottages by relatives and friends for a few weeks when they were not being used. I've had patients who were given holidays as gifts by their parents and even their bosses. One of my patients who had been on social assistance for years because of a disability, inherited money and was able to take his first vacation. Another patient, also on social assistance, was treated to a free trip by her boyfriend. It helps to think positively and keep dreaming.

When you do want to go away on a holiday, what do you do? Call up your trusted travel agent? Or do you get together with friends or acquaintances that have been away and get their advice? Before my wife Bonnie and I go away on vacation, we make it our business to speak to everyone who has been to the place we are going. We take detailed notes and carry the recommendations with us on our travels. Since we have traveled so frequently we have become "experts" ourselves, so we sometimes sit down with future travelers to chat with them about sites to visit, what to pack, what to buy, where to stay and what delicacies to enjoy.

We began writing things down for our friends and got excellent feedback from people about how our travel tips had helped them save time and money. There is camaraderie among travelers. Getting together before trips with people who have been away is a lot of fun and makes fears and concerns melt away. Coming home and showing your sensational purchases, trinkets, and photographs keeps the spirit of traveling alive and provides endless evenings of good cheer.

As I began to exchange stories with people I collected amazing tales of how their trips had affected their lives. This mirrored my own experience and I found myself becoming more and more interested in travel therapy. That interest has culminated in the writing of this book.

Unfortunately, I cannot sit down with each of you personally and help you plan your vacation, but I've put together my thoughts, feelings and expert advice on what you need to think

16

about to get the most out of your holiday.

The first half of this book looks at how traveling and vacations can help you both mentally and physically, and how being away from the daily routine can change the course or direction of your life or reaffirm your life's choices. In these pages we will look at why people travel, what motivates us to leave home and set out on a journey. I also hope you will pick up pointers about how to make your trip more rewarding and memorable.

The second half of this book is a collection of travel articles that I wrote as a way to record my own experiences. People tell me these stories make the far away places more real and motivate them to visit their favorite places. I believe it is this sharing of stories that encourages many of us to set off on our own journeys.

Have you ever been told that you need a rest? Do you keep putting off getting away because you think you don't deserve time off? Or are you just afraid to leave your present rut for fear that it would all collapse if you left? Some of us take ourselves so seriously we believe we are indispensable. Indeed, the most important thing is the wish to get away. You must dream your vacation in order for it to happen. It is important to plan ahead and put a date on your next vacation, even if it is years into the future. This gives your dream substance.

I am appealing to you nomads and explorers who still have that restless wish to look around and see how the world looks. Not only will I share some of my own personal revelations, realizations, and new beginnings, but also I will relate other stories from my own patients and friends that will exemplify how travel is HELPFUL and HEALTHFUL.

CHAPTER ONE
HOLIDAYS ARE HEALTHY

Since my graduation from medical school in 1973, I have met many patients whose lives were changed irrevocably by holidays. I've seen tremendous improvements in their physical and emotional health after they came back from vacation.

The more I enquired about their travels, the more I became aware of the many positive transformations taking place. I could also often tell if a medical problem was of a serious organic nature because it would not usually disappear while someone was on vacation. If a problem did disappear when someone was away, the illness was likely stress related, and being away was enough to either eliminate or sufficiently diminish the stresses and relieve the symptoms.

Take Norman Yan, a 51-year-old applied ecologist and professor at York University, who has a deep understanding and concern for the environment. For the past ten years, he has suffered from seborrhoeic dermatitis, an inflammatory skin disease that affects his scalp, nose and chin. This condition causes redness, itching and scaling. When he was on a two-month vacation in New Zealand and Fiji the rash disappeared. When he returned home, however, his rash was back within three weeks.

Although Norman's recovery could have been a result of climate, environmental or dietary changes, he feels the condition is stress related and being on vacation was the cure — at least temporarily. Now Norman recognizes that when his rash flares up he is under a great deal of stress. In fact, he relies on his skin condition as a monitor to tell him he has to make positive changes in his life.

Then there is Andrea, a 27-year-old, green-eyed, satin-skinned dental hygienist, who tortured me one day by cleaning my teeth. While she scraped, prodded, poked, and rattled my skull with an electronic scaler, she told me how a holiday had made her healthier.

During her first year of work she developed a painful, stiff neck. Her job involved sitting in one position, often bent over her patients, and this was straining her neck. She went to her physician who prescribed a non-steroidal anti-inflammatory drug, but this didn't seem to help. She was sent to a physiotherapist, whom she saw for over a year but with little relief. Andrea also went to a chiropractor, but he also couldn't relieve the pain.

Finally she and her husband went on a one-week vacation to Club Med. She felt relaxed and let loose. After swimming, dancing, sun bathing, and acting like a teenager again, she realized that her neck felt better. By the end of the week there was no more stiffness or pain. Now years later she is still relatively pain free, even though she still works as a dental hygienist. She attributes her recovery to that one-week vacation.

Svetlana is a 46-year-old Russian mother of two, whom I met while in the Soviet Union in 1974. It was a cold, damp, August evening and I was camped in Kalinin, a town between Leningrad and Moscow. I spent three hours talking to three Russian students who were studying English. It was mind-boggling to learn how these students felt about sex, divorce, alcoholism, war, politics and violence. Their upbringing and education were so markedly different from mine, yet the essence of their hopes, dreams, and feelings were identical to my own. We had so much in common, and I felt invigorated, talking into the wee hours of the morning.

For many years, Svetlana and I kept in touch. In 1988 the USSR loosened its travel regulations and Svetlana, for the first time in her life, stepped outside the boundaries of her country and visited West Germany. She later wrote: "It was the first time I traveled without my children, and I was filled with some extraordinary feelings, inside forces, and good spirits. I went along the streets smiling, and was full of goodwill toward everyone I saw. Usually I get bad headaches almost every day, but during the two-week vacation I had no pain at all. I became calmer, and felt full of life and more myself. This trans-formed feeling lasted the whole year."

I personally often visualize a peaceful scene to help me relax. Invariably I think back to a time I was on a nude beach on the Greek Island of Mykonos. There was a faint, fresh, breeze tickling my naked body as I stretched over a cool, smooth rock. Surrounding me on all sides was the crystal-clear, turquoise Mediterranean, lapping at the sunlit, sandy beach. The sky was aqua blue and cloudless, and the sun warmed me like a tepid sauna. Every now and again when I became too hot, I reached over into the chilled sea and splashed myself with refreshing water.

Every half hour, a small, grey fishing boat with a sputtering engine would pass the rock with a boatful of skimpily dressed young tourists, eager to rip off their clothes and join the hun-dreds of naked bodies soaking up the sun on Paradise Beach.

On Mykonos I felt somewhat exposed, yet fantastically free, my senses alive with colours, sounds and feelings. It was a relief to take off my bathing suit. I felt so far away from home, so anonymous, so carefree. My breath was full of sighs and my eyelids fluttered.

I rested on that rock for hours.

20

I often think back to this special time and place as a way of coping with the stresses of my life today. I also flash back to other special places I've visited. They are anchors that help to arm me for day-to-day living. Twenty minutes of reliving these experiences is often enough to spark a different feeling inside me, and help me cope with the challenges of being a physician, father and writer.

COPING WITH STRESS

When you are healthy, you are physically, emotionally, psychologically, and spiritually in balance. You are in harmony with your external environment, you feel good, your body's systems are functioning properly, and you are free of pain. Stress can upset this natural balance and cause dis-ease. Usually these stresses are in your external environment, and how you react to the demands they place on you determines your level of comfort.

Sometimes when you are under stress you know your body is not working well, but you are so swept up in things you are blind to this fact. Even worse, sometimes you know what the stressful factors are, but you are so overwhelmed you just can't cope. You are in the midst of a battle but you can't seem to change your battle plan to meet the onslaught or retreat from the skirmish.

In one study researchers measured the blood pressure, heart rate, and levels of epinephrine, a neurotransmitter released by the brain, in participants during both days off work and days at work. They found that all these measures were reduced when participants were at home. As well, holidays of only one or two days were found to have a positive impact.

Getting away helps us distance ourselves from the stressful parts of our lives. If your job has been overwhelming, your relationships too demanding, or your lifestyle unhealthy then getting away can be a tremendous relief. It can help restore your perspective, give you new viewpoints, and allow you to develop new coping strategies. Simply being out of your stressful environment can make you realize just how crazy your life has been, and increase your resolve to make changes.

One of the oldest prescriptions for living a balanced life comes from the Bible and the fifth commandment. By keeping the Sabbath and making it holy, you restock your mental, physical and spiritual cupboards.

Interestingly, most modern day medical prescriptions contain rest as an important element in recovery. Intuitively we recognize that when we are sick it is important to rest the body to help fight the illness. If you have an infection, a fracture, a heart attack or any other serious disease, then time off from work is mandatory to aid the healing process.

Historically Greek, and traditional healing systems of India (like Ayurvedic, Unani and Siddha) all emphasized the need for rest to become healthy.

Greek shrines of healing were often located far from the village, in scenic countrysides. Greek physicians advised patients to travel to these hospices to rest, and to get away from the rigors of home life. Epidaurus was such a hospice sacred to Aesculapius, the Greek god of healing and attracted thousands of sick pilgrims.

Aulus Cornelius Celsus, a famous Roman doctor, advised his patients that a long sea voyage and a change of air were effective for the treatment of tuberculosis. He especially recommended the voyage from Rome to Alexandria. Avicenna, a

22

renowned Arab physician, also recognized that a change of environment was important to help patients rid themselves of disease and sent them away on healing trips.

PREVENTIVE BREAKS

Preventive breaks are vitally important to help you avoid getting sick. The body, in its wisdom, gives you messages to slow down. If you ignore these messages and keep over-working, or maintain a stressful lifestyle, you may well get sick and be forced to slow down — for a long time. In some cases it takes a life-threatening illness to force people to change their lifestyles.

Taking a vacation is one of the best ways I know to break the pattern of daily stress. Don't wait until you face a serious illness before you re-evaluate your life. Researchers Mina Westman and Dov Eden from Tel Aviv University, adminis-tered questionnaires to 76 clerks who had a two-week vaca-tion, and they found that burnout decreased significantly during their vacations.

Linda Hoopes and John Lounsbury, researchers in the Department of Psychology at the University of Tennessee, sur-veyed 128 employees before and after they had taken a vaca-tion. They found that the workers reported a significant increase in life satisfaction after they took a vacation.

A national study of more than 2000 adults in Finland looked at differences in the use of vacation time between peo-ple who had migraines or other types of severe headaches and those without headaches. Seventy-six percent were inter-viewed on their vacation. Headache sufferers were found to have less interest in vacations, whether paid or unpaid. They seemed to be unable to relax and enjoy themselves.

But we all need to do this if we're going to stay healthy.

Take Linda. She was planning her daughter's wedding, which she worried would drive her to distraction. The white-haired, rosy-cheeked nurse lacked self-confidence, had a tendency to look bleakly into the future, and was apt to get herself tense and fearful about upcoming events. She realized she would be a mess when the wedding finally took place, so months in advance she wisely booked a one-week holiday to Bermuda two weeks before the wedding. During her vacation she was able to forget about the wedding, and when she returned she felt refreshed and rested. She was in a good frame of mind and was able to enjoy the final week of preparations.

Some people plan a vacation at a particular time of year because they know that just prior to taking off they are at their busiest and, therefore, prone to getting sick or burning out. For example, accountants in North America are busiest in March and April because that is the tax season and they are under considerable stress.

Sheldon, a 50-year-old successful accountant, works like a dog from February to April. He puts in 16-hour days, works seven days a week, skips meals, and rarely sees his family. He has learned to plan a two-week holiday in advance in early May, when the tax season is over. This gives him something to look forward to and he can use the rest to recharge his batteries. His wife also knows that there will finally be an end to his working around the clock and that they will be able to spend some quiet time together.

Many teachers choose teaching as a profession because it offers them holidays during Christmas and Easter, as well as summer vacations. Even though teaching is stressful, they know that they will get time off to rejuvenate. Indeed, the philosopher Bertrand Russell said that one "advantage of work was that it makes holidays more delicious when they come."

REST STOP

Stooped, frail, round-shouldered, and pasty white, I was exhausted physically and emotionally, and 10 pounds over-weight. I gazed back for the last time at the huge brick hospi-tal, which had been like a prison to me. I had entered my internship bright-eyed, excited and a little frightened at the prospect of treating patients for the first time as a full-fledged doctor. I never thought the year would be such an ordeal, and the hospital that I had longed to work in would suck me dry and leave me crying inside.

I wasn't angry anymore; I just felt relieved. While walking away from the hospital on that last day, I pictured some of the images of the past year. I remembered weekends on call, from Saturday morning to Monday afternoon, with only four hours sleep; being shaken awake at 3:00 a.m. to trek to the wards to sign an order so that a nurse could give an aspirin to a patient with a headache; resuscitating a heart-attack victim for the third time, praying he would survive; pronouncing strangers dead in the middle of the night and having to tell shocked, sur-prised relatives, who were never informed that their loved one was dying; stitching up pitiful, thankless, drunken bodies, always at two in the morning, one after another in the emer-gency; holding open surgical clamps, during a four-hour tor-tuous orthopedic procedure, while the surgeon sawed, scraped and hammered away.

Somehow I survived.

By the end of the year Bonnie guided my heartless, exhausted, worn-out shell of a body out of the grounds of the hospital, back to our cozy apartment to pack our bags to begin our 14-month journey around the world. On July 10, 1974 we said goodbye to relatives, friends, material possessions and responsibilities and took off on our rejuvenating voyage.

The trip was just what the doctor needed. I lost the 10 pounds, relit the shine on my skin, brightened my eyes, toned my muscles, and got myself into the best physical shape I had ever been at any time in my life. Most significantly my enthusiasm for life was rekindled, my curiosity reawakened, and I had the peace to re-dream my dreams and rethink the direction of my life.

I was reborn.

LIFE IS TRAVELING

For some people, traveling is a way of life. There are vagabonds who never settle down, and whose life would be a living hell if they couldn't get away. Floriano Steiner is an ex-photographer who lives in Asolo, at the foothills of the Alps in the northern part of Italy. He lives in this small town from April to November, but when the leaves start to fall, the days become cooler, and his luxurious garden begins to fade, Floriano becomes clinically depressed. He so identifies with the changes around him that his whole mood changes from one of life and renewal to death and decay. He says the only way he can avoid being hospitalized or put on medication is to take off each year and travel to a hotter climate where there are lush, green plants growing, a sun high in the sky, and the warmth to expose his whole body to the air.

In 1975 I first met Floriano in Kuta Beach, Bali, an island in Indonesia. He was one of a community of travelers who lived in Kuta. We hung out together, went to small, quaint restaurants, frolicked and relaxed on the expansive brown-sand beach, saw technicolour breathtaking sunsets, played music and shared tales of philosophy and living. We sat for hours under coconut palms talking about our journeys and our experiences.

After we left that paradise, we continued to write back and forth, and were lucky to have him stay with us for a few days in 1988. Floriano, a child of the Great Depression, is big-bellied and talks in a rolling, resonant tenor voice with a half Italian, half Austrian accent. His eyes sparkle as he talks about getting away to survive.

"I'd most likely be dead if not for traveling. A trip to Rio de Janeiro is much cheaper for me than even a short stay in an insane asylum, of which I am a veteran anyway. I have chosen my climate ever since I was 24 when, for the first time, I had this incredible experience that I no longer had to be enslaved by the unavoidable following of the seasons. At all times, all year round, I could find a climate congenial to my health, mood, and lifestyle."

"So even when I was living like the worst bum, having no money whatsoever, I adapted my talents to the possibility of travel by becoming a photographer, because as a photographer I could travel and survive."

For the past 20 years Floriano has felt deep in his heart like a pauper, still the product of the Great Depression. As a child during the war, he used to beg and steal in order for him and his family to survive the bleakness of Europe during the German occupation. His past continues to haunt him, and he still goes to the market each Saturday to get the leftover fruit that the merchants will be throwing out. He also goes like clockwork to the butcher for bones and to the cheese merchant for the rinds that would normally go into the garbage. He hates to waste anything and is obsessive about throwing anything out, even though he is now financially better off.

"When I feel the arrival of cold air, I become very depressed, and I'm reminded of the time when I was working as an insurance agent in Cologne, Germany, where every morning I would pray that it would already be Friday night. Then one day I figured out that this was the greatest waste in the world. For two days I felt like living and for five days I felt as if I was cursed. As a consequence, I gave up my job and started traveling, and I've been traveling ever since. Some animals hibernate in winter; for me hibernation is a waste of time. I'm not like a bear: I'm a bird. Travel keeps me out of mental hospitals, and it prevents me from having to take drugs and see a psychiatrist. My therapy is light and sunshine. It's also much cheaper to live in warm climates, like most of the poor people in the world."

Floriano moves about his property naked, raking the leaves, trimming the flowers, and cleaning the pond.

"The greatest richness of all the possible treasures is friends. To befriend people of all creeds, colours and religions will make you cosmopolitan, and will give you an understanding of the greatness of cultures and ideas all around the world."

"The incredible feeling of freedom to choose my season like a bird who crosses thousands of miles on the sheer strength of its wings, will-power, and instinct has become a necessity for me. People say traveling opens one's eyes; however, going away gives me eyes. I wouldn't need eyes to live every day in the same environment, but constantly changing the sites, the

28

scenery, and the atmosphere, has sharpened my eyes and all other senses. It makes me truly alive."

There is another advantage to traveling, says Floriano, and that is education. "Some people say it broadens our horizons, but I say it makes one realize what the horizon stands for in the fullest sense. It makes you discover every day that the world is not flat. And yet most people live as if the world is flat; they live their lives like they are doomed to stay in the same spot. The world itself is traveling in the universe, and the stars, the galaxies, the blood in our bodies are moving. The most natural activity a human can do is to move."

Floriano Steiner never needed any encouragement from anyone to find the time to get away, even when he had little money. He always managed to travel. What does it take to get you to take a vacation? How long do you have to work; how many hours do you have to put in; and what do you have to accomplish before you give yourself permission to take a break?

I've known people who say they will work really hard for however long it takes until they have saved enough money to retire, and then they'll have time to travel. Although they keep working their hearts out, they never seem to get around to retiring. Something always comes up. Then when they are finally prepared to retire, they get some catastrophic illness and can't enjoy their time off.

There is no better lesson than your own mortality to convince you to take a break.

Getting away can make you realize just how fortunate you are. You suddenly have a different appreciation for all the things you are doing that are helpful and healthful. Absence also makes the heart grow fonder, particularly if you are traveling to countries that are poverty stricken. You begin to appreciate proper sewage, clean water, and a choice of foods that you once took for granted.

There is a famous Japanese saying: "For the spoiled child the best medicine is to send him on a long trip."

CHAPTER TWO

TRAVEL – A CATALYST FOR PERSONAL GROWTH

I remember feeling amused when my parents would run into someone they had not seen in 25 years and remark, "You haven't changed a bit." However, as I think about some of my old friends, I realize my parents were right.

Take Jeremy. Now in his forties, Jeremy is identical to the way I remember him when he was eight years old. That's because the essence of your personality stays the same over time. That's not to say, however, that you can't change the way you view the world — and your own life.

Have you ever left home on a holiday and returned feeling like a new person? Usually this lasts for a few days or weeks, before old patterns re-appear. However, many times some of the changes can be more permanent.

When you're at home you see yourself in the context of your day-to-day environment. You play various roles at work, in your family, and with your friends. For example, in your family you may be the "princess," the "baby," or the "black sheep." Everyone identifies with you in this role, and even though you will likely outgrow it many people will treat you as if you haven't changed. Similarly at work you might be the "boss" or the "brown noser" or "lazy bones", and even though you may not enjoy the label, once you are seen in a certain light it's difficult to change your identity. One of the best opportunities for a new perspective and personal growth is when you are far away from the labels that have been attached to you.

When you are away from home, you have a chance to drop

31

your personal history and meet people in a fresh way. You get to travel incognito. Often you meet people from different cultures and backgrounds and so you develop or rely on different aspects of your own personality. This frees you to do things "out of character".

Remember what it was like to move to a new neighbourhood and new school when you were a youngster? In a sense you were starting over, which can be both scary and exciting. The teachers didn't know you, the children in your class were strangers, and your new neighbours probably had no idea what you were like. In a way, taking a vacation is like moving to a new neighbourhood.

Many of us so strongly identify with our labels, which have become such an integral and central part of our personality, that we cling to them. Our religion, nationality and political beliefs can overwhelm who we are as a human being.

Ever meet someone who wanted to tell you his or her life story the moment you are introduced? "Hello, my name is George. I'm a married father of four, Protestant, conservative, dentist from Michigan."

People like George feel most secure when they have labels to give their life structure and themselves a personal history. Without labels, George and his cohorts feel as if they have no unique identity. With no identity, they feel lost.

I believe the opposite is true. Without any labels, you begin to explore your real self — who you are at the core. When you strip yourself of all your social labels you get back to the essence of you. You can always stick the labels back on later, but try dropping them while on vacation.

I remember sitting in an old, three-story, country house overlooking a tall oak tree with Sandy, a 59-year-old owner of Century House, a bed and breakfast in Bracebridge, Canada. Sandy had oyster-coloured skin and an animated, raspy, expressive voice. She jumped at the opportunity to tell her story.

She felt that travel significantly changed her perspective on life, and brought forth personality traits that had not been dominant before. On an 18-month exploration of herself in 1984, Sandy traveled to Europe, the Middle East, Asia, and Australia. Because she left behind her support systems and all the security she thought she needed — a good job, close family and friends she was able to develop her own internal resources.

"When I was traveling, I often didn't speak the language; I had no idea where to stay; and I didn't have the comfort or security of home. What I realized though was that I had my health and my wits about me," Sandy said.

"I realized that people were basically helpful wherever I went. So I became less worried about security, less materialistic, and less afraid of talking to people I didn't know. This has had a lasting effect on my life. Even today I'm not willing to fall into a rut just for the sake of security."

Before her journey of discovery Sandy had been a shy and withdrawn person. She was miserable working as a medical technologist for the government but didn't have the internal resources to let go of such a secure position.

As Sandy sat across from me at her old, dark-oak dining table and chatted away she did not, by any standards, seem shy. She explained the transformation.

"After landing in Australia with only $25 to my name, I picked up the Sydney phone book and started phoning hospitals. Within one day I had three job offers. My self-image and self-confidence were uplifted and improved. Whereas I had turned to outside sources for help before, I chose on this occasion to turn inward for support.

"The trip," she added, "meant learning to appreciate both my weaknesses and strengths. I found I liked myself. My self-esteem and self-worth continued to grow as the trip progressed. I left all the 'shoulds' from the external world and my personal history behind. Then I could figure out what was important and relevant to me. I am no longer governed by what other people expect of me; what's important is what I expect of myself. The good and bad experiences completely turned my life around. Anything bad that happened served only to strengthen my character."

Most of the time we view vacations and travel to be an outward journey, where we learn about the world and the people around us. For many people, travel has always been an inward journey and, rather than only discovering the external environment, they have also focused on their internal world.

Do you ever feel you are on a merry-go-round and you don't know how to get off? I call this the "rut syndrome". You become so busy living your life, or surviving, that you never get a chance to think about your life. Have you ever worried that you would wake up one day when you were sixty and wonder what life was all about? You'd look around and realize that you never went anywhere or did what you really wanted, and you let the years zip by without directing things.

Vacations can be a way to jump off the merry-go-round and take a close look at yourself and your life. It sometimes takes a few weeks to slow down and bring some perspective to the things that have been happening in your life. Many people make some important decisions and realizations while away from home. But it doesn't have to take a few weeks. Sometimes even a weekend break can solidify, clarify and identify areas in your life where changes are necessary.

Vivian Darroch-Lozowski, a professor of Holistic and Aesthetic at the University of Toronto and author of "Notebook of Stone" and "The Voice of Hearing", mesmerized me when I first heard her speak. The fresh and vibrant way that she talked, reminded me of a young girl. I remember, particularly, her joie de vivre.

"My life, for me, depends on foreign itineraries," she said. "I will go somewhere only when there is a draw to that place of my being. Thus I went to Ladakh, India because I wanted to know 'the dry'. I am now preoccupied with that 'I was here before there was language,' hence, my plans to go to Antarctica, which is the most language-free place on Earth (because it is deterritorialized).

"Foreign itineraries serve me as 'others' with whom I may engage. I never find rest when I travel. I find endurance, penance, and hardship. I find through this effort that I begin to glimpse, through the 'other' of the foreign place, what is in me but which I had not seen before. The ecstasy of travel for me is its very ordeal and the clarity I find in the small moment-to-moment progressions of it. I learn about myself through the arcs of flight that link all my destinations. Before I depart, my attentions are amorphous, even ambiguous. I never travel with an itinerary. I wait to see what will open itself before me after I arrive and as I am moving through the landscape. I am never disappointed. All journeys increase my self-knowledge. More importantly, they allow me to better understand how I may live in the present-day. When I return from wherever I've been, I feel cleansed, I feel stronger."

SYNCHRONICITY

In 1981 Bonnie and I spent a few days on Beachcomber Island, a tiny island in Fiji surrounded by a white-sand beach. There we met Barry and Sylvia Rabinovich. He was a respiratory physician who had just finished his post-graduate training. He told me about a 68-year-old doctor who worked day and night for years. He finally decided to retire and take it easy. Three months later he was dead of a heart attack. It's not an uncommon story I've come to discover.

Barry, bearded and muscular, has a knack for getting down on his hands and knees and playing wholeheartedly like a child. He strengthened his resolve to get the most out of life.

"After my medical training I took a six-month sabbatical and traveled extensively around the world. Before my journey I was truly a type A personality preoccupied with work. After being exposed to different cultures and seeing the way the world operated away from home, I had a different perspective on what I wanted. I realized that there was more to life than medicine, and began to shift my priorities to have more leisure time. Although I still enjoy my work, I am more well rounded, less time focused, and more able to relax. Traveling brought a new dimension to my life."

Amazingly enough, two months later, in Kuta Beach, Bali, we bumped into Barry and Sylvia again. We ended up spending more time together exploring Bali and hanging out in the waves. It was another example of synchronicity and one of the great joys of traveling — coincidental happenings and meetings that seem to infer that there is more than just chance at work. It is a common experience of travelers who report re-meeting fellow vagabonds in the most unlikely places, and it has happened to us often. Whenever we renew acquaintances unexpectedly, we are doubly rejuvenated, and reminded that many things are happening beyond our conscious awareness.

In December 1974 in Nandi, Fiji we met a Canadian couple from Toronto who were on a world trip like ours. We only had time to sit and eat some ice cream cones together before we went our separate ways. Four months later, Bonnie and I were driving a motorcycle to a secluded beach on the island of Phuket in Southern Thailand. When we got there we found Sean and Pat sitting on the beach, almost as if they were waiting for us.

Pat was a 22-year-old teacher when she took a sabbatical to visit Europe. She explained, "Once I got there moving around and meeting new people, I discovered I didn't want to be tied down to a job. I didn't want to get married so quickly, and did not want to settle down into a routine. For many years, I never took a job that I had to commit to for more than a year. I found traveling so exciting, fun, and romantic, that it changed my mind- set, which had said that at age 22 you should get married and have two children. Because of that trip I continued traveling and it wasn't until eight years later that I did settle down, and got married."

Try to explain this chance meeting. We arrived in Hong Kong on April Fool's Day 1975 and we didn't know where to stay. We took a bus from the airport to a high- rise hotel complex called Chungking Mansions, which had a different hotel on each of its 10 floors. We weren't sure which one to choose, but in the elevator we met a couple, Jack and Lynn, from Los Angeles who were staying at one of the hotels. They advised us that except for the cockroaches, their room seemed fine. We checked into their hotel and later spent a few hours talking to them, sharing travel stories.

The next day we checked out of the hotel to stay with some friends, but hoped to see Jack and Lynn again someday, although we had not made any plans to get together. Well, three days later we were taken to a fancy restaurant called the Golden Crown, which had four floors of rooms, each floor subdivided by beautiful Chinese screens. There were hundreds of tables and, yet, to our amazement we were escorted to a table right next to Jack and Lynn. This time we exchanged addresses of where we would be after Hong Kong, and even talked about leaving messages for each other in Nepal.

From Hong Kong they went to Bali, and we went to Thailand, Burma, and Calcutta. Six weeks later we boarded a Thai Airways flight in Calcutta to find Jack and Lynn sitting on the plane smiling up at us. They had boarded the same plane in Bangkok. We decided that the universe had meant for us to be together and ended up spending the next four months in Nepal, Kashmir, Afghanistan, Iran and Greece with them.

Fourteen years later we conspired to meet Lynn in Kashmir on the same houseboat that we had shared in 1975. The Houseboat Potamac is a huge, two-bedroom, intricately carved pine boat that was moored on the quiet waters of Nagin Lake. All around were mountains, with the snow-capped Himalayas visible on clear days. We sat in the living room, which afforded us a clear view of the lake and the hills on the distant side. We could hear the mosque across the lake calling its faithful to prayer. The floors of the houseboat were covered in fine, colourful, hand-knotted Kashmiri carpets and, as Lynn spoke, she rubbed her bare foot back and forth across the patterns.

"For my whole life I had been in a 'large cage,' doing what was expected of me. It was as if I was in a cocoon waiting to turn into a butterfly. I was a 23-year-old college student when I decided to break out of my shell, explore the world and see for myself what was out there. Everything about my world had been extremely familiar. I was a successful A student, involved in many extra-curricular activities, and was very popular. I had always been around people and situations that defined me and told me who I was. On this trip for the first time I was thrown into a situation where nothing was familiar and nothing told me who I was supposed to be."

She paused to sip her Kashmiri tea, which we had become accustomed to drinking with the local bagels and cookies. It was one of the luxuries provided twice a day for guests. Lynn flipped her silky, blonde hair, cleared her throat with a tiny cough, and continued, "I was really like a lame person who had always used crutches but didn't know she could walk on her own. Without my supports and without my whole world looking at me and telling me who I was, I discovered I really didn't know who I was. I had no idea how insecure I was until I was traveling alone in foreign countries. This trip was really a journey inside myself, and it was truly disorienting."

"I began to reflect on who I was and what life was all about. After four months into the trip I was in a little hotel in Sicily, feeling shy and alone. I was so embarrassed about my need to be with someone that I decided I didn't have what it took to travel around the world. I was going home. Up until that time I had always seen myself as strong; had always been perceived as aggressive, competent, and talented. So for me to come to a place where I felt so lonely, insecure, scared, and inadequate was an amazing self-realization. Without my external supports, the internal supports were not what I had always imagined them to be."

39

"Traveling had brought me face to face with the truth about myself, which I don't think anything else could have done. I got hold of myself and instead of flying home I began to break out of my shell and started talking to people. I made a couple of good friends, and instead of fleeing to comfortable surroundings continued on my trip. Being able to survive and develop my own support system was an extremely important lesson for me. My life changed dramatically. When I did go home after being away 10 months, I was stronger, more resourceful, and a more secure person in a more genuine way."

I was fortunate enough to see Lynn again, in her role as competent psychotherapist and mother to her daughter, Mariya. As we sat on the patio of her home in the hills of Malibu, overlooking the blue Pacific, she sipped a glass of white wine and said, "Traveling has always meant throwing myself into the unknown, and in so doing finding out who I really was. I discovered that a lot of the assumptions that we all make about what we need to have to live and be happy are just assumptions. I learned through my travels that I could live in appalling conditions, with few material possessions, even under semi-dangerous situations, and still be exquisitely happy.

"Traveling through Asia made me realize that as many people and cultures as there are in the world, there are that many ways of being alive in the world. And there are as many different points of view that define what is meaningful and makes life worth living. I became particularly aware how our culture defines our beliefs and our personal reality. If you looked at me now, living in my house in the hills of Malibu, driving my nice car, wearing my fancy clothes, you wouldn't know that on the inside I look at this entirely differently. I know inside that none of this is important or essential in making me satisfied. I have learned through being away that I don't need all the things that I once thought I did to survive and be happy. Traveling forced me into an internal journey that changed my way of seeing everything. Traveling has been one of the very best ways to perpetuate my internal journey and has helped to keep me vital, alive and growing."

Lynn, Susan, Pat and the other people you've just read about are living examples of what can happen when we travel. Getting away helps us get in touch with our true selves, lifts our sagging spirits, give us the time and space to make clearheaded decisions to alter our lives in positive way. Holidays can indeed be a catalyst for personal growth.

CHAPTER THREE
DEAR DIARY

Summer vacation has just ended. It's your first day back at school. Your teacher tells you to write about "My Summer Vacation". You mull over what you did for the last two months and write an interesting story sharing what you learned and what fun you had.

Marco Polo, Christopher Columbus, and D.H. Lawrence, I'm sure, were never asked by their teachers to keep a travel diary, yet they along with thousands of writers and explorers kept a journal of their adventures, recording their day-to-day experiences, thoughts and feelings while away from home. Few of us are travel writers and may not think we have profound experiences to share; however, the act of recording our observations while on holiday can serve a useful purpose.

Most people take photos and video movies to capture on film the highlights of their trip. It's fun to show your friends what a wonderful time you had. It's also true that a picture is worth a thousand words. Sometimes, however, a thousand words are worth a picture.

Keeping a travel diary can be a more personal account than any photograph album. It can serve as a memory to keep forever, and help to mark moments on your path through life. You might use it to look back and see what you were experiencing and thinking at a particular point in time.

Some people keep a travel journal to record the day's events, money spent, food eaten, and people's addresses. While there is nothing wrong with recording factual information, perhaps more useful and interesting is to keep track of feelings and impressions and to use your journal to become more introspective.

Sometimes the direction you wish to go in your life becomes obvious when you are away. Incidents and circumstances happen to change your view of yourself and the world. Everything seems to fall into place. You don't have to work hard at becoming more conscious of yourself. Other times it is necessary to sit down and actually examine your life, and plan out your future with respect to growth and health. When you are away is a good time to conceptualize first what your life is like and then how you wish to change. A diary can help you do this.

Have you ever written down thoughts that were swirling in your mind as a way of making decisions? I have seen many patients who at times had overactive minds and so many thoughts that they became anxious and had difficulty sleeping. The preoccupying repetitive and persistent thoughts interfered with their enjoyment of life. I asked them to write down on paper whatever came into their awareness. Once they put it on paper, and even if they had to write the same thought again and again, eventually with time their mind would become still and less active. Getting the thoughts down visually and organizing them helped to bring everything into focus.

If you haven't already done so, buy a diary or journal before your next vacation. Choose a book that looks appealing, will survive the test of time, is small enough to fit in your pocketbook or hand luggage, yet large enough to suit the length of your vacation.

It is important that if this book is to be more than just a budget record or a recording of day-to-day events, it must be personal and not read by anyone else but you. Understand that this is your own and not for sharing. You may have to hide it or lock it in a secure place. Sometimes getting a diary that you

43

can lock is necessary for you to feel secure enough to write down your most secret thoughts. Also know that what you write doesn't have to be true. It can be fantasy. You have the freedom to put down whatever pops into your head.

FEELINGS

While on vacation in Jamaica, Connie Mason was feeling angry but she didn't know why. She certainly wasn't angry at the never-ending sun, crystal-blue ocean, or rhythmic-reggae dancing. Since there was little in Jamaica to account for her anger she thought maybe it was left over from the past. She took out her journal and experimented with writing down the words "I'm angry at ...," and then made a list of the people in her life. Beside each name she wrote what she might be angry about. Next to some names she wrote a few lines, while next to other people, such as her mother, she wrote a whole page of resentments.

Since Connie was in a tropical paradise, and feeling quite safe and relaxed she was able to empathize with the people she was angry with and also realized that being angry only made her feel worse and didn't get back at the person who triggered her anger. She didn't phone up all the people on her list and scream at them, but instead began to examine how she could begin to forgive the people for their insensitive and inconsiderate behaviour. She visualized the people in her mind and saw herself telling them exactly what she was willing to forgive.

She also looked at the part she played in creating the anger. She realized that she often said "yes" to things she actually did not want to do and resented this afterwards. But if she said "no" she felt guilty. So Connie explored on paper the changes she wanted to make in dealing with these people and with her anger. She realized it was okay to stick up for herself and not let others take advantage of her. She also realized that it was okay to be self-protective.

The journal exercise put Connie in touch with her feelings and relieved the burden of anger that she had been carrying. The diary allowed her to take an intimate look inside herself.

A journal is meant to be free-flowing and spontaneous. Generally in our society people keep their emotions in check. Some of you may find it difficult to express positive or negative emotions in a constructive way. You may have difficulty getting in touch with feelings of joy, love, anger, hate, fear, sadness, jealousy and happiness. Feelings that are left unexpressed often have an effect on our physical well-being. In particular, this internal tension affects the autonomic nervous system. Psychosomatic diseases like migraine, asthma, irritable bowel syndrome, or hives can sometimes be aggravated as a result of feelings that have not been expressed. Writing your feelings down may be a first step toward sharing your emotions more openly and freely with others.

As an exercise write down the words joy, sex, love, jealousy, fear, hate, anger, sadness and guilt. Next to each word write down your associations with these primary emotions. All humans have these emotions at one time or another. Write the names of the people in your life who you associate with these feelings.

Now ask yourself this: What can I do to make the most of the positive emotions in my life and resolve the negative?

DREAM ON

Some people remember their dreams more easily while on vacation. Fritz Perls, the father of Gestalt therapy said, "the dream is the most spontaneous expression of the existence of the human being". He believed that every dream is a projection of the conflicts and unfinished business of who we are. Instead of interpreting and finding symbols, he had people re-experience the dreams as if they were happening in the present. He asked people to act out their dreams taking on the role of every aspect of what they remember. Perls thought that by playing the different parts, people would get in touch with fragments of their personalities that were dissociated and not acknowledged. By role-playing they would bring the unconscious to conscious awareness and in the process dis-cover themselves.

Try keeping your journal on your nightstand and in the middle of the night or first thing in the morning, write down the details of the dream. Record every person, object, mood, smell and sound that you remember. Then go through the dream as if it is happening now and begin to re-experience it in the waking state. You may wish to act the dream out loud with a friend or on your own.

Draw a rough picture of the dream. Take some of the items or characters of the dream and become that thing, acting their part. Closely examine the conflicts or unfinished parts of the dream. Then develop endings and solutions. You may also want to share your dream with another person that you trust and talk about your impressions. This has an added bonus: it brings you closer to the person you're sharing your dream with.

GOAL TENDING

As I've noted before, being away is an excellent time to regroup and take a new look at your life. After you've arrived at your destination and have a quiet moment take out your travel diary and answer the following questions: How would you like to change your life? What are your goals? If you had three months to live what would you do with your time? How would you like your life to be different now, in six months, in a year and in five years? Use your journal to write down whatever comes into your mind.

The idea of setting goals will help you work towards the changes you want to make. These may deal with work, family, and friends. It's a good idea to write down each of your goals in these areas — and others — spelling out your short-term, intermediate and long-term ambitions. Explain how you hope to accomplish these goals, and specify the steps or stages that will be necessary to make them happen.

Many people have trouble with goals. They don't even want to try because of past failures. We've all had New Year's resolutions that were never carried out. It's not that we were insincere when we made them but often our aspirations were misguided. Goals need to be reasonable and realistic.

Unreasonable goals lead to disappointment and frustration. Mary, a 38- year-old, single secretary, was a perfectionist and always disheartened herself by setting goals she was unlikely to reach. She lost hope even before she started. For example, Mary wanted to lose weight, start exercising, get married and switch jobs. She decided to lose 30 pounds in one month, exercise 30 minutes a day and find the right husband within 60 days. She was doomed for failure.

47

Mary tried to do too much too soon. It might have been more reasonable to take smaller steps. A goal of two pounds a week or exercising for 10 minutes three times a week is more achievable. But Mary had to learn to lower her expectations.

Be sure to make your goals specific. Otherwise how will you know when you have accomplished it? How will you know when to celebrate?

For example, you might generally want to be more spiritual. That's a wonderful quest. But your goals need to be more concrete. Perhaps your goal is to meditate or pray for 10 minutes every other day. If you prayed for longer or more often then you might consider giving yourself a special reward. Similarly you might also set a minimum standard such as praying for five minutes.

Remember even though you didn't reach your desired goal you still worked towards it. Don't feel guilty. Goals train you to feel like a winner and should not be used to put yourself down or encourage you to retreat back to bad habits.

EXAMINE YOUR STATE OF HEALTH

Are you healthy? Take a close look. Assess your physical, emotional and spiritual well-being. Determine what you are doing to harm yourself, then outline what you can do to change this. Also figure out what you can do to ensure you will move toward a healthier lifestyle.

Make a note of the five major stresses in your life. What and who makes you the most uncomfortable? More importantly, how do you perpetuate these stresses and what can you do to change the circumstances or the outcomes?

Being away is an ideal time for a health check. You have

more uncluttered, uninterrupted free time to identify problem areas and start down the road of change before you return to the hectic pace of home. As well, there are important decisions to make that may be more difficult to make when you are submerged in the chaos of work, family, and friends.

For instance, if you are having trouble deciding whether to get married to a particular individual, take a two-week vacation alone. How do you feel when you return? The space and time away may clarify your feelings.

If you are thinking of changing jobs, going back to school, or ending a relationship, getting away from it all can help put things in perspective. Writing down your thoughts on paper while you're away can lead to finding solutions.

MEMORIES

It's a good idea to take a close look at how important vacations are in your life.

Recall past trips and write down in chronological order each holiday that you've taken noting when you went, where you went and with whom you went. Record changes you made in the way you view things, or live in the world, as a result of those holidays. What happened to bring about these changes? What did you learn about yourself? What were the high points?

You don't really travel to change, you change because you're traveling. Keep a diary to record your dreams, goals, thoughts and innermost feelings. It can help get the most of your holiday and be a treasured record of your memories that can complement any photo album.

CHAPTER FOUR
TIME TO WORK ON RELATIONSHIPS

LETTUCE ALONE

What is the favorite salad of a honeymoon couple? Lettuce alone.

In many cultures it is customary for newlyweds to go away on a honeymoon? It's seen as a special time for them to get to know each other better both physically and emotionally without all the demands of home life.

In North America, the nuclear family used to be the building block upon which our society is based. So it has always been imperative that the marital unit be strong. Our culture understands that to begin a committed relationship a couple needs time to be with one another. We also understand that its best to leave the newlyweds alone at this time. Often the honeymoon location is kept a secret so no one will be able to disturb the couple or take away from their time together.

The "honeylunacy", as it was once called, is like starting fresh, establishing the context of the marriage to come. It also allows the couple time to recover from the tension and busyness that often takes place before the wedding.

I am reminded of Beau Vallon Beach on the island of Mahe in the Seychelles, a country in the Indian Ocean. About 10 fishermen in a small, wooden boat dragged a large net in a semicircle away from the beach. Everyone stopped what he or she was doing to watch what was happening. As the men tumbled from the boat hundreds of shiny, silver fish were jumping out of the water, escaping from the net.

The men dragged and pulled; the semicircle got smaller

until they brought it closer to shore, capturing hundreds of large, struggling fish, some three feet long. Tourists everywhere were snapping photos, children were grabbing at the fish and the fishermen were filling a waiting truck with their catch.

It was there on this beautiful island overlooking turquoise waters that I met Judith and Alfred, newlyweds. She rollicked topless in the waves, while he lay outstretched on the soft, caramel-coloured sand soaking up the sun's rays. When they got married their parents had given them a choice between having a large wedding or using the money to take a month's vacation of their choosing. They gladly chose the vacation. They had been staying in the same house we were and because there was a common toilet, my three-year-old son called them "the people who were living in our washroom."

Even though they had been living together for 18 months before they got married, this time away together had taught them much about their relationship. Alfred, bearded, slightly built, ex-musician turned salesman, talked about discovering how important it was to consciously provide space for each other and give one another quiet time alone. Back home there were always distractions. On Mahe, living in one room and doing everything together, they learned that when they started getting grumpy instead of fighting they would go for a walk on the beach — alone. By the time they met up again the bad mood had invariably passed. This awareness of their need for quiet time hadn't been obvious at home where there were other distractions.

Another young couple, Julie and Sam, both in their early 20s, decided to take an extended vacation for nine months. Although they were not newlyweds, this trip occurred early in their marriage. During this trip, because they were together 24 hours a day, they discovered many new things about their spouse — and themselves. In fact, they realized they really weren't well suited for each other and their vacation led to their subsequent separation and divorce. But both Julie and Sam were grateful that they discovered this incompatibility early in their marriage, when they could heal fairly quickly and when no children were involved.

Barbara and Frank had been living together for a year before their extended vacation. It became evident after only three days that they had completely different expectations of the trip. As a result the couple went from talking about marriage to seeing one another as strangers traveling together. They really hadn't understood each other until they began spending much more time alone together. Barbara, for example, hadn't noticed Frank's avid interest in other women and hadn't realized how selfish he was until they embarked on their voyage together.

Many couples feel they are compatible until they spend day after day together without the distraction of work and the support of friends and family. Traveling together may cement a relationship. It may also destroy it. People sharing the same challenges and experiences will often feel closer. But spending a long, uninterrupted stretch of time together lets you see all aspects of someone's personality. This is why many couples that are planning on getting married spend an extended period of time together.

John and Michelle went on a trip around the world. They had been married for three years and thought they knew each other well. Their journey began on board the famous ocean liner, the S.S. France, which took them from New York to Paris. It was an extravagant — and elegant bon voyage. In Paris they rented a car and traveled to Scandinavia.

Michelle, blond, blue-eyed, freckled, recalled that, "From the time we got off the boat, we started arguing about everything. I liked to get up early and get going while John liked to laze around. I was concerned about money; John was a spendthrift. We argued about where we would eat, sleep, and which photo to take. We seemed to be on opposite sides all the time. This was strange because we rarely had disagreements in the three years we had been married. We both felt stuck and saw no way out.

"Maybe it was the stress of packing up, saying goodbye to everyone and leaving home and the fears we had about our expedition. Maybe it was a power struggle and neither one of us was prepared to give in. Perhaps it was anger and resentment that had been stored in each of us that never got expressed because there were all the distractions at home. When we were alone, those feelings came out. Things went from bad to worse.

"We were in Stockholm, Sweden after being away for two weeks. We had a huge fight about John buying cherries, which I felt were much too expensive. He sat on the lawn, eating the bag of cherries while I ran back to the room crying. We felt like this was the last straw. I was thinking of turning around and going home. I didn't know how we were going to spend another minute together. Back home there was always someone to talk with and get advice. Here we were isolated, feeling alone and left to our own resources. We stayed away from each other the rest of the day, giving one another the silent treatment. Somehow we agreed to go to a movie called "Papillon," a marvelous film about two convicts who were suffering such pain and hardships in prison. They were stripped of their freedom, forced to survive on insects, and treated like animals. Dustin Hoffman and Steve McQueen played their roles superbly. Their loyalty and growing friendship contrasted starkly with our reality.

"We were two young adults, completely free, with access to everything we could want, living in relative luxury, yet arguing day and night. Something about the contrast between our situation and the movie, the emotional portrayal by the actors and the meaningful story affected us deeply. We cried and felt transformed. When the movie ended, we both stood up and hugged each other. Our hostilities and resentments melted away. From that moment on, for the next 13 months we never had another argument. Left to our own resources, away from outside influences, having no other supportive relationships we had to confront our separateness and resolve our conflicts. The movie and the experience became a powerful symbol and lesson for us. Never before and never since have we had such a test of our relationship."

Many couples use a romantic interlude to rekindle the romance in their marriage. It doesn't take a lot of time away to re-ignite the sparks. One partner may book a hotel room, buy fancy lingerie, send flowers, a loving card, and order a bottle of champagne. The two meet in the hotel bar and pretend that they are illicit lovers, having a final rendezvous for one special evening. Candlelight, room service, and a warm bubble bath together. Everything is set for romance.

FRIENDS

You don't have to be married or living with someone to travel with them. It's nice to have someone to share experiences with, to be able to reminisce with later and to be there in case of trouble. The trip can often make friendships blossom.

But just as you choose the type of vacation and the destination with care, you must also choose your traveling companion with care. Nothing can ruin a holiday more quickly than being stuck with someone with whom you are not getting along.

Rose, a gray-haired, 78-year-old widow, who lives alone in a small bungalow, was planning all year to go to Miami, Florida for a two-month holiday. She unfortunately chose a roommate who "got on my nerves." The two women were just not compatible. Rose liked to get out and do things, while her friend wanted to watch T.V. Rose had relatives she wanted to visit but her roommate got insulted if she wasn't included. Rose was on a strict diet and there were heated disagreements about what to cook and how to cook it. Rose was a clean "freak;" her friend was sloppy.

Needless to say, the vacation didn't turn out as well as Rose hoped. Even more sadly, a friendship that spanned five decades came to an abrupt end.

Jim was a first-year university student when he decided to travel to Europe for one summer. He didn't really have anyone to go with but didn't want to sow his wild oats by himself, so he finally chose an acquaintance that he didn't know very well.

Now a successful lawyer, slightly balding, wearing thick, horn-rimmed glasses, he told me, "We had an incredible time together exploring almost every country in Europe and doing it on $5 a day. Yet our time together wasn't always smooth. We were both fairly stubborn, wanted things our own way, and were preoccupied with our budget. But we learned to compromise, focused on the positive aspects of our journey and came home good friends. We learned a lot about the way the world lives and about each another. Our friendship was cemented on this vacation and it's now lasted more than 30 years."

FAMILIES

Being a parent in this busy, demanding world is difficult. We have to deal with working, shopping, cleaning, paying bills, going to the bank, spending time with friends, and answering the phone. They all interrupt the uninterrupted time we need to spend with our children. There is no better way for any family to grow closer than to spend time together away on holiday.

Many couples don't enjoy traveling with children because they feel children interfere with their time away and so ironically 'it's no vacation'. Also many parents feel it may be unfair to uproot the kids.

When friends heard Bonnie and I were traveling to Asia for four months with our three boys they responded almost as if with one voice: Isn't it dangerous? If my child ever got sick I would feel so guilty. Children need the security of their own home and friends. My kids wouldn't eat the food. How can you deprive their grandparents from seeing them for such a long time? It's hard enough traveling without having the hassles of children to spoil the fun. How unromantic!

All these objections have an element of truth to them. Traveling with children is more complicated. There is an element of risk. Having kids sleeping in the same room does interfere with romance.

However, the benefits of traveling with kids far outweigh the disadvantages. Have you ever felt that your children are growing too fast? Are you so busy there's little time left to spend together as a family? Are you worried that your children's friends have a greater influence on them than you do?

I see many families where the father is so busy the children rarely see him. In other families the rush is on to get out of the house each morning. Then everyone scatters in different directions for the rest of the day until they bump into each other again at dinner.

Traveling together can put you back in touch with your family in a way that's not possible at home. You and your partner will have more time to sit and chat about what's happening in your lives and in the children's lives. You can begin to work together more co-operatively and consistently.

Dr. Stuart Hill is an entomologist and professor of ecology in Sydney, Australia. His only memories of spending time with his father were during summer vacation. Most of the time his dad was working and had little time to spend with the children. Stuart says if it hadn't been for those two weeks each summer, he would never have known what his father was really like. It was an invaluable time for son and father.

A young mother, Betty Antreskis, asked me to recommend a book to help her discipline her child. The book, "Children: The Challenge" by Rudolph Dreikurs, discusses approaches to child rearing and specifically dealing with behaviour problems. She and her husband took it away with them while on holiday with their son and read it together each day.

Since they were away and there were no other diversions or time pressures, they were able to devote much more attention to helping their three-year-old son Alex. They talked about the changes they could make, especially in terms of how they reacted to his temper tantrums. They agreed to set limits and began to be more consistent. Their relationship with each other also improved because of what they shared.

Another family I knew was having a particularly rough time together. The parents were constantly arguing; they even slept in separate bedrooms. Their two children were misbehaving at school and difficult to manage at home. Principals, teachers, psychiatrists, social workers and me, as their family doctor, were all involved.

The family finally took a three-week summer vacation to France and Spain and a change began to take place. They were together 24 hours a day. Since the parents were not at work they were able to pay constant attention to their two boys. The children finally got the supervision and extended contact they had been longing for.

When the family returned home the parents were more open with each other. They even began to share the same bed again. The children were more relaxed and less anxious and upset. Teachers, social workers, and psychiatrists were amazed at the transformation. The vacation was a catalyst for a positive change.

There is a certain intensity that occurs when you are on holiday together that is so difficult to attain when you are at home. This is why I recommend vacations as a therapeutic way to build healthier marriages, families and friendships. The time away doesn't have to be fancy or expensive. The important component is the chance to be together and have fun.

CHAPTER FIVE
EDUCATION IS A TRIP!

I was a quiet, polite, spoiled, teacher's-pet kind of eight year old. I traveled by car with my parents and another couple south for three weeks from Toronto to Miami during the December holidays. I remember clearly insisting that the reason I was taking a holiday was because I needed a rest. I wasn't sure what I was resting from: mathematics, skating, my older brother — but I had a distinct feeling that this was an opportunity to laze around and forget about all my eight-year-old responsibilities. I cherished the time with my parents and leaving the shelter of suburbia for the first time was exciting.

As we drove through the United States and got farther and farther into the Deep South, I heard accents and ways of speaking that were remarkably different from what I had ever heard before. Although the people were talking the same language, it became more difficult to understand what they were saying. We were in the heart of Georgia and my father needed to go to the toilet. We pulled into a rickety, old gas station to refuel and use the facilities.

My father asked, "Could you please tell me where the wash-room is?"

"Pardon me, sir?" replied the grimy old gent who was working the pumps.

"Can you direct me to the bathroom?" my father repeated.

"The what?" the unshaven attendant replied, looking very confused.

"You know, the toilet!" said my father, beginning to squirm a little, the business at hand becoming more urgent.

"I don't understand," was the answer.

By this time my father was frustrated and I was watching in disbelief.

"Where is the powderoom, the men's room?" pleaded my dad, crossing his legs, trying to prevent an accident.

"Powder room?" queried the toothless old guy still not understanding what we wanted.

"The shithouse!" screamed my upset father. "Where is the shithouse?"

"Oh, the shithouse. It's right out back. Just turn to your right," the old man said, relieved at last to know we could speak his language.

By this time all of us in the car were in hysterics, doubled over with laughter. I had an experience with accents and the variety of ways the English language could be spoken, that I would never forget.

The images of poverty, rickety, old shacks with broken roofs and clothes hanging out to dry stay with me to this day. Going down South, my first time leaving Toronto, I began to appreciate that there was a complicated, unpredictable, colourful world out there. Leaving the shelter of my protected neighbourhood, my narrow world enlarged and expanded. I learned more about geography and history on that three-week trip to Florida than I would learn in all the books at school.

WHY ARE WE HERE?

Many people feel that they have no purpose and their life has no meaning? One reason we are alive is to discover who we are and find our true mission. If you are interested in evolving as a person, then the more you learn about yourself and your environment, the more you grow into a fulfilled, mature human being. The more you know about the world, the better you will learn how to survive in it. There is no better way to learn about yourself and the world than to get out and explore it.

One of my favourite stories about the philosophy of spiritual development is about Siddhartha, or Buddha, the Enlightened One. He was unhappy in his father's house even though he was a royal child and had all the material comforts possible. He left home on a journey of discovery. That journey led to his Enlightenment. He could not have transformed his life if he remained in his father's palace.

Even in the Old Testament, Adam and Eve were forced out of the protection of their home in the Garden of Eden, to learn about the real world of good and evil. Moses and the children of Israel left Egypt and wandered in the desert where the 10 Commandments and the new laws were given to them.

Jesus, who was born in Bethlehem, traveled to Egypt with his parents before they settled in Nazareth. During his life he journeyed from Nazareth to Jerusalem, through the Galilee, into the wilderness and across Israel to understand the world and his role in it. Mohammed, who spent most of his life in Mecca, went with his uncle on business from the time when he was a young boy. Those experiences helped to shape his character. It was on the road from Mecca to Medina that he had an epiphany. This religious experience was the foundation for the development of Islam. Mohammed said, "If you have to seek knowledge travel anywhere."

Literature is also filled with stories like Ulysses, Gulliver's Travels, Pinocchio, and Huckleberry Finn in which unlikely heroes set off on journeys of adventure and self-discovery.

Of course, you do not have to travel to learn about yourself. You can develop inner strengths and resources without ever leaving your neighbourhood. But getting away, encountering new life experiences fosters growth; it makes change and learning happen more quickly and intensely. When you are away from the distractions, routines, and daily habits of home life I believe you learn better.

All animals have a natural instinct or curiosity to explore their surroundings. At first through sight, but eventually through taste and touch, human babies discover their world and how to survive in it.

At about six months of age babies begin to crawl. They go on their first travels. By age one, when they're starting to walk, they're on the verge of being full-fledged explorers. Everything in the home is fair game. This is when parents have to tuck things out of reach or lock them away in cupboards. I remember my days as an emergency room physician examining children who had swallowed pills, cleaning fluid, and coins or who had broken limbs from falling from places where they shouldn't have been. Their natural curiosity is not only a potential threat to babies themselves but priceless vases, unlocked cars, important papers are all targets.

When children begin to speak they ask questions about everything. The desire to understand their world is a survival mechanism. They're very good at it. Have you ever been around a four year old with the "why disease?" All day, everyday, the child asks "why?" Everything needs to be explained down to its smallest element.

THE WORLD IS OUR CLASSROOM

The word education comes from the Latin root "ducere", which means to lead or to draw forth. Education is the process by which each generation learns the things that were known to the generation before them. Thousands of years ago, before formal education, young children learned how to live in the world directly from their parents. If they wanted to learn to hunt, to farm or do a particular trade, then they apprenticed with someone who could teach them. Often this meant leaving home.

Most formal education now takes place in schools. Teachers try to bring the world to the classroom. They also use the world outside as their classrooms and take children on field trips and exchange programs to experience a different culture. It has also been customary for students to travel away from their home in order to study subjects that were not available in their hometown.

It is not always practical to take a child out into the world to learn. Certainly most forms of formal learning are facilitated today by teachers trained to motivate and support their students. As parents we do not always have the same level of skill and ability. However, I still believe that if we travel with children, keeping in mind the school curriculum, then we could teach children all that is necessary about history, geography, languages, and even mathematics.

Every travel experience can be used to teach our children about the world and about themselves. I am not suggesting that every trip has to be a formal lesson in learning. Children, like adults, resent having to do work on holidays. However, if attention is paid to the questions that are asked and what the child wants to learn, it doesn't have to feel like work. Learning away from home can often be a less tedious process.

The chances of remembering are also improved the more senses that are engaged in the learning process. When children are actively involved in learning then they will recall what they have learned more effortlessly and effectively.

Some people learn best visually. If they see something written down they can remember it recalling pictures in their mind. Other people remember best when something is said out loud. They recall the information by repeating it silently to themselves, or hearing the information replayed in their mind. Others learn kinesthetically through touch or feel. If they write something or feel it with their hands they can recall it more easily. When you travel all your senses are involved and learning is optimized. This is why sometimes incidents and events that take place during a vacation are never forgotten.

George, a 43-year-old real estate agent with a never-ending smile, curly black hair and intense brown eyes, sat beside a roaring, crackling fire in his suburban home and told me about his travel experiences with his family.

"Each year when we take our children out of school to go on a trip most teachers are excited by what we are doing. They feel that the children will experience things that they could never learn in school. There is no better way to learn about geography than to travel to different places and see the area in person. We drove through five countries in Europe with our kids and were able to teach them about the countryside in a way that they could never have achieved by simply reading about it. Now when they do study it in school they will have a real-life experience of what the places were like."

I remember how difficult it was for me to picture the differences between rivers, oceans, lakes, bays, islands, and peninsulas until I saw them with my own eyes. My vision of the world is not based on what I learned in school but is almost entirely based on what I have seen, heard and experienced in my life.

How much easier it is to understand how Niagara Falls

generates electrical energy when you visit the Falls and see how the water turns the turbines and the wires take the current away. I could have read about the outback of Australia but it wasn't until I spent 23 days camping there in February the hottest month of the year that I truly appreciated what it was like.

Cheri Shore was an 18-year-old high-school student when her parents took her out of school to travel to the Orient. Her current studies teacher assigned her a project to write about each major city she visited. This made the trip even more memorable for her and the hands-on research was more detailed than any library at home could ever have provided. Will she remember this project when she is 64? You bet.

Besides geography, history also comes alive by visiting places in person. History from a book can be quite dull. But not when you visit the sites where the events took place.

When I first traveled to Japan I was transformed. I had heard and read stories of the destruction and suffering that took place when the atomic bomb was dropped on Hiroshima on August 6, 1945. But I don't think I could ever have understood exactly what happened until I visited the Peace Museum and the Peace Memorial on the spot where the bomb hit.

Seeing the city, touching the memorials, watching the films, touring the displays, and speaking to the men and women of Hiroshima made the horror of nuclear weapons painfully clear. Spending the day there has created in me a level of awareness that will never be erased. I walked the city and marveled at the indestructibility of people's will. I looked in the faces of the elderly and wondered where they had been when the bomb struck. What suffering did they have to go through? Are they still suffering from it?

I became terribly sad. I spoke to people about their

memories and discovered a recurring theme. How could the Americans have dropped the bomb at a time when they knew everyone would be out in the streets? Couldn't they have waited until people were in a shelter? Wasn't the message clear enough without destroying thousands of lives?

As a physician, I was also moved by the magnitude of the pain and suffering. Eighteen hospitals were destroyed. Ninety percent of the doctors were either killed or injured; most of the nurses died. People within a radius of four kilometres were struck dead or lay dying. The city was instantly leveled in a thermal flash and roaring blast. I was sickened to read about the effects on the human body.

That vacation changed my thinking about the threat of nuclear war. It also convinced me to act. Indeed, my experience in Japan led me to establish an organization of physicians committed to ending the use of nuclear weapons. I helped start the Canadian branch of Physicians for Social Responsibility along with Dr. Frank Sommers and others.

Education is more than geography and history. It includes learning about other cultures, other religions and other ways of life. It also includes learning about art, music and dance.

Where you may choose to go on vacation may depend on what you're looking for spiritually, psychologically or physically. Some people go on religious retreats and sequester themselves in a monastery. Others go to growth centers like Escalen in Big Sur, California where you can take workshops to improve your self-esteem and sense of well-being. Health spas are a popular choice today. You can pay more attention to your physical and dietary needs. Then there are conventions or conferences whose themes coincide with your particular needs. For example, spend three days giggling and laughing at the

Therapeutic Effects of Laughter and Play Conference at Saratoga Springs New York and you'll return home with a brighter, fun-filled attitude.

When we travel to far away places we realize that all life is interconnected. Native or aboriginal people often have developed their understanding of the world through spiritual vision and life-science observations of the natural world. When people understand they are not separate from the natural world they will seek to honour and understand it.

Native people have traditionally understood the Earth has a mind and a spirit and a cosmic intelligence that responds to our intentions. When people no longer learn from the land, their disconnection leads to abuse of the Earth. Perhaps it is this disconnection that has led to contamination of land through deforestation, pesticides, industrial waste, radioactive poisoning as well as water and air pollution. Traveling across the land, seeing the incredible scenery, being aware of traditional societies and the impact we have on our environment helps to make us more aware of the fragile nature of our world.

LEARNING NEW SKILLS

Education is also about learning new skills, including indulging in hobbies and playing sports. If you've ever gone on a sports vacation you know that you can cram a lot of learning into very little time. If you want to learn golf, tennis, skiing, or scuba diving many resorts and hotels specialize in these sports. You can get an all-inclusive package that includes unlimited opportunity to play your sport or a package of lessons that will help you to learn the sport of your choice. Other sporty holidays include mountain climbing, white-water rafting, bicycle touring and sailing.

My friend Jerry is a unique man: both a rabbi and a psychotherapist. He has a special interest in the therapeutic effects of dreams and past-life regressions. Jerry spoke with me about a holiday he fondly remembers.

"In the winter of 1976, when I was 40 years old, I was in the final stages of a marital break-up. It had been a very difficult and painful experience. My emotional health was at an all-time low and physically I had seen better days. The cold had arrived, the snow was falling and I was beginning to dread the prospects of winter.

"I had begun to date other women, a decision reached at mutually by my wife and myself, giving her, of course, the same freedom. One woman I was dating asked me if I wanted to go skiing. I told her that I didn't know one end of a ski from the other. I had always thought skiing was a sport for the wild and woolly, not to mention the images I had of casts and crutches. But even though I had grave misgivings I immediately said yes to her idea of a week at one of the best ski schools in North America.

"I found myself at the top of a wide, long, white ski run and I wondered why I had agreed to this insanity. By the end of the day I had made it down this run many times and by the end of the week I had entered the final-day races down one of the most advanced runs. When we left the next day I looked up at the trails again, only this time with a sense of pride and satisfaction. More than this I felt exhilarated, strong and healthy. I look back over the years and count the many ski trips I've had with my friends and children. I look forward with eagerness and excitement to the first snowfall.

"In retrospect, that first ski vacation has had a tremendous impact on my life. It was an emotional and physical high that helped me through a difficult time. I now go through the winter with a very positive attitude and a strong sense of well-being. I have only one regret — I wish winter lasted longer."

MOOREA MOMENT

Bonnie and I didn't really enjoy the island of Tahiti all that much, but the outer island of Moorea was beautiful and relaxing. Perhaps the most memorable thing about Moorea was that was where my son Larry learned to swim.

Nowadays there is a tremendous emphasis placed on sending children, even young infants to swimming lessons where they are taught how to float, to put their head in the water and to swim. We were staying at the Moorea Hotel in a lovely round hut overlooking a pristine ocean. Larry who was 3 years old at the time, liked the water but, as yet, had never been able to float or swim.

We took a 20-minute boat ride to two islands just offshore from our hotel. Here, between the two islands, was a large coral reef and the most incredible multi-coloured fish we had ever seen. When we put on our goggles and fins and began swimming between these two islands, it felt like we were in a large fish tank; the tropical fish were swimming along side us. Angel fish, parrot fish, tiger fish, incandescent blue fish and other rare fish were everywhere. Furthermore, there was beautiful coral of every color of the rainbow and water so clear that nothing obstructed our view.

Larry also began to be interested in the fish, so he put his head in the water to look at them. The next thing we knew he was putting on a snorkel and mask and dipping his head under the water. Much to our surprise he began floating on his chest with his bum up in the air so he could get a better look. He soon began to float, his head under water watching the tropical beauties.

We had some leftover bread so we began feeding the fish, and soon some sparkling, white fish were coming fairly close to shore to gobble up the bread. Larry giggled and laughed and there, on the island of Moorea he began to take his first strokes and swim under water. It was so natural, so easy. We didn't have to show him or coax him. He did it spontaneously because he had a purpose: he wanted to see the pretty fish.

After we left the reef, we took Larry to the swimming pool at the hotel and had him swimming back and forth between the two of us as the sun set overhead casting a fiery red orange glow on the pool, the beach out front, and us. In one day my son had learned to swim 20 feet. From that day on, at every beach and in every pool we visited, Larry improved his ability to swim.

A few months later we were on a house-boat in Kashmir, Northern India and we paddled out to one of the boats in the middle of Nagin Lake. The water was about 40 feet deep and Larry, who was then about three and a half years old, was swimming around like a fish in the middle of the deep lake without fear and without our concern, since at that point he was a very good swimmer. He even jumped into the water off the top of a houseboat and swam around with us like a real porpoise.

After we returned to Toronto, we enrolled him into Junior Kindergarten. Part of the curriculum included swimming lessons so they took our little porpoise and put him in a class with other 4 year olds. The instructors began to teach them how to put their heads in the water and blow bubbles. There were many children in the class who were extremely frightened and did not want to go into the water and started to cry.

Larry, seeing their fear and their tears, began to also be apprehensive in the water and because the teacher treated the whole class the same, Larry began to regress and soon was clinging to the side of the pool like the rest of the children.

Much to our amazement, even though we told the instructor that Larry could swim lengths of the pool with ease, she paid no attention and started him back on the basics of learning to put his head in the water and blow bubbles. Within a short time Larry stopped swimming. It wasn't until six months later, when we were again on holiday, that Larry regained what he had lost in those swimming classes.

I've always wanted to recreate this type of situation. I'd like to put children in a pool with fish and encourage them to put their head in the water to see the fish. The focus would not be on learning to swim but on seeing the pretty fish under the water. As a natural consequence the kids would begin to float and then swim.

A vacation is often an excellent time to teach children new skills because everyone is usually more relaxed and there is more time to concentrate.

There is also no better way to expand your knowledge of the world than to go out into it. Politics, language, and religion come alive. Everything you've read about is put into perspective. Traveling promotes harmony and understanding. The world becomes a smaller place. Borders break down and people are brought together.

TEACHING TRUST

Many people are xenophobic. We distrust people in general and especially people who are different from ourselves racially, culturally, or religiously. Sometimes parents teach their children not to trust anyone who is not family.

Deep in our souls we know that we are all of the same essential core and although there are many external differences in the way we talk, look and act, people from all over the planet seek basic human needs. When you receive warmth and kindness from strangers and people who are supposed to be your enemies but turn out to be your friends, it changes your outlook. It teaches you to trust.

Rather than sending out armies or political delegations, countries should be sending out tourist ambassadors to make contact with people on a one-to-one level and establish links that build co-operation.

Time after time on our travels, my family and I were the recipients of the warmth and kindness of people in the least expected places. From these experiences and contacts I have faith about the potential in the world for peace and harmony. Traveling helps to build that faith.

CHAPTER SIX
ARE YOU A TOURIST OR TRAVELER?

What's the difference between a traveler and a tourist? The word "travel" is derived from the French root "travail" meaning work. It implies that going from place to place is not easy. Until this century, travel for most people was unpredictable, difficult and dangerous.

A tourist is like a traveler but is more often externally directed and guided rather than being independent and free. Tourism and sightseeing often go hand in hand, along with cameras, souvenirs, guidebooks and American Express cheques.

Two thousand years ago people did travel long distances to visit famous shrines, spas, and temples. They even visited the seven wonders of the ancient world and marveled at the sights. The first group travel started with the pilgrimages to Jerusalem, where the faithful visited the famous Biblical sights of the Old and New Testaments.

Mass tourism as we know it really began in 1841 when Thomas Cook chartered a train and carried 570 teetotalers for a reduced fare of one shilling each — from Leicester to a temperance rally 11 miles away. Cook was the first real travel agent and with him came the birth of tourism. Soon he was arranging group tours to Scotland, Paris and across the Atlantic.

Now in many third world countries tourism is the largest industry and employer of people. Many countries depend on tourist dollars to survive. When there is a political crisis or natural disaster like earthquakes, hurricanes or floods then fears are often that the tourist industry will be affected. Billions of dollars worldwide are spent on promotion and advertising.

For some people the word tourist has negative connotations. Recently, government agencies sensitive to this began removing "tourist" from their promotional material and replacing it with the word "visitor". Being a tourist offers great potential to promote understanding and peace in the world. There are many advantages to being part of a guided tour.

ADVANTAGES

Perhaps the biggest advantage is that you are looked after. You sign up for something that interests you and the rest is handled for you. You will often be advised about what to pack, what vaccinations to get, what health precautions to take, which countries need visas and what will happen from day to day.

Usually you just have to get to the airport, bus depot, or train station, and from that point on you and your bags will be taken care of. Often independent travel is a struggle. You have to pour through maps, read up on which sights to see, and then figure out how and when to get to them. On most guided tours all that has been predetermined. Knowledgeable guides, who have researched the history and culture of your destination, are there to tell you all about it. The day is booked and travel prearranged. If the meals are part of the package you don't even have to search for a restaurant. You will usually be taken to a place that caters to Western tastes. You will feel like you're at home.

Often because things have been prearranged and the guide has been there many times, you can pack much more sightseeing into a day than you could if you were doing it for the first time and on your own. Furthermore, tour guides deal with any surprises and complications. They are comfortable dealing

74

with the unexpected and have solutions and alternatives ready. I am not ignoring the fact that many times expectations are not met, cockroaches are scurrying around in the rooms, promises in the brochures are broken, and tour guides are indifferent. However, most tours are satisfying, convenient, and worthwhile.

Another benefit to traveling in a group is the company of the people involved. Being part of a tour group is a wonderful way to meet new people and make long-lasting friends. Often the friendships don't end when the trip is over.

If you are a single person or have health problems traveling with a tour group is a practical and safe option. If you've never been away or are going to some strange and unsafe area, a tour can give you the structure and security you need. There is safety in numbers. Somebody will be looking out for you. If the guide does a head count and you are missing someone will set out to find you. If you are elderly or have health problems you will also feel much safer being part of a group.

Some people like to be part of a tour the first time they visit a destination. This way they can sample a little of everything the place has to offer and later can go back on their own.

There are also many destinations that are extremely difficult to go to without a guide. For example, traveling in China on your own can be quite challenging if you are not an experienced traveler. Few people speak English and tourism is still undeveloped. Most people go on safari to Kenya with a tour company because seeing the animals properly and safely is difficult without an experienced guide. Traveling through the outback in Australia or mountain climbing in Nepal is also difficult when you try to do it on your own. Even taking a day tour of a large city like Delhi, London or Jerusalem is extremely arduous without the help of an expert.

TOURIST TO TRAVELER

Sandy was the owner of a travel agency that specialized in travel for senior citizens. He told me a story that underscored the importance of a tour group for some people. In this case traveling with a group had a dramatic effect on Florence. Sandy smiled as he related the story.

"When Florence first walked into our office to inquire about our upcoming group tour to Hawaii she fit the stereotype of a dowdy old lady. She was pale, slightly hunched over and never smiled. She had a lot of questions about the tour, most of them coming from a skeptical, cynical point of view. She sat and read the entire travel insurance policy and had lots of 'what if' questions pertaining to its coverage. She had a big fear of the unknown. Many of her questions showed a lot of mistrust. It seemed like Florence was going to be a real problem traveler.

"The next time I saw Florence was in Hawaii at the end of her two-week vacation. She was in the lobby of the hotel with her arms around the shoulders of two traveling companions. She wore a brightly coloured Hawaiian Mu-mu, a flower in her hair and a smile from ear to ear. She came over and gave me a big hug and laughingly told me about her experiences and gossiped about her fellow travelers. She was beaming and didn't want to go home.

"I had never seen such a transformation in a person. The trip obviously had a tremendous impact. Florence became a regular traveler with us and soon began taking our more adventurous tours to the Orient, South America, Egypt and other places. Now she is a favourite of our group leaders."

TRAVEL WITH INTENT

Many travelers go on journeys to transform their life and way of seeing the world. Dr. Robert Burns, a vascular surgeon from New York extols the virtues of "Experiential Travel". He went on a trip with Andrea and Gary Smith who take explorers on a special kind of vacation. Dr. Burns says that his trip with Andrea and Gary "changed my life". "Since coming back I've begun to see the world differently. I appreciate the spiritual aspect of my personality and have become much more aware of my creative energies."

Andrea Smith is a world peace artist, painter, philosopher and mother of two children. Her home is in Lahaina, on the island of Maui in Hawaii. She has led numerous travel adventures to Egypt, Bali, Thailand and Tibet. Their holidays attract people who have an interest in peace, love and art and enjoy being in special locations in the world.

"Many travelers are interested in visiting spiritual environments to gain insight and knowledge. Our groups are warm, intimate and always filled with laughter. It's like traveling with a family that has no Karma," says Andrea.

Andrea's husband Gary, a former pharmacist and present social director of the travel experiences elaborates, "There are people who just don't want to be tourists but want to be pilgrims or pioneers visiting special spiritually charged power points on the earth. These locations are impregnated with a living energy. If you travel all by yourself you have to look after the worries of travel. Our guided vacations attempt to look after all the details. It's for people who like individual travel but want someone else to make decisions about where to go and who to talk with to get the most of the experience. Our trips create intimacy with the environs, culture, and people of the land that you could never get on a large group tour. It is designed for those interested in uplifting their spiritual heart as well as keeping their physical body in comfort."

Andrea who has dedicated her art to spreading love and peace explains, "The trips are another way of sharing my joy, love and way of seeing the world. I never enjoyed traveling in groups but preferred to be on my own with Gary. I never realized the benefit of group travel until we went to Egypt on the first journey. I got the benefit of sharing wonderful moving transformational experiences with others. Everyone is drawn to these groups for different reasons. We seem to attract loving people who return home with a new perspective and awareness. Everything I do and believe in is about finding inner peace and remembering who we are at the core of our being. It's really about remembering as opposed to finding something you have lost."

Some of us are phobic about change. We want familiarity and stability to feel secure and comfortable. We enjoy the routine of knowing what's going to be happening from day to day, hour to hour, moment to moment. We appreciate schedules and regimens and don't like surprises. The very thought of being footloose and fancy free is frightening. There is nothing wrong with being a tourist and there are many advantages to being part of a guided tour. But every vacation starts with a dream.

First the dream, then the booking, at last the trip and finally the memories. Begin to dream about your next holiday today.

CHAPTER SEVEN

PRACTICAL TIPS TO MAKE HOLIDAYS BETTER

In the first part of the book I focused on how traveling is good for you. This chapter will give you some helpful hints to make your vacation even more enjoyable.

PACKING

Have you ever sat in front of your suitcase, shifting clothes around, wondering what you should take and what you should leave behind? Have you ever tried to stuff extra clothes into an already full valise and watch the zipper tear from the pressure? Do you get into screaming fights with your children or partner about the kinds and quantities of clothes they are taking?

Then you arrive at vacationland only to find that you didn't pack what you need but did bring everything that's completely inappropriate. Wouldn't it be nice if there were a checklist?

Packing is a hassle. You have to picture your holiday in advance and imagine what you'll need. The length and type of your vacation, the climate of your destination, and the amount of luggage you can bring determines what you will pack. Obviously going away for a weekend to a family wedding at a fancy hotel in New York City demands different clothes than trekking the mountains of Nepal for three weeks. A longer voyage, where you might be in different climates and cultures, requires yet a different wardrobe.

The following advice assumes you are going on an extended journey through different climates; requiring different levels of dress; and having moderate luggage capacity. You can alter these suggestions to suit your own specific needs. If you are going for longer than two weeks, then pack for one or two weeks and be prepared to wash everything from time to time, re-using the wardrobe in different combinations.

Most countries will have laundry and dry cleaning facilities either through your hotel or, more cheaply, around your hotel or on the main street. Often the service is fast and inexpensive. You can also hand wash your clothes with cold water in the sink and leave them to dry overnight.

If you are going for less than two weeks and staying only in one climate zone, remove the clothes I have listed in the following pages that don't apply. For example, don't take a raincoat if you are going to spend two weeks in the desert.

Some people need very few material possessions to feel comfortable. Others can't seem to leave home without taking everything but the kitchen sink.

HELPFUL HINTS

Take along clothes that match each other in colour and style, so most tops can be worn with most bottoms. Pack 100 percent cotton clothes or cotton with a small percentage of polyester (permanent press that never needs ironing). If something wears out, you can throw it out or give it to a local person in need. Some people take clothes they don't care about and feel good leaving them behind with an appreciative inhabitant.

There are many types of luggage to choose from. I do not, however, advise taking an expensive-looking suitcase that would attract thieves' attention. As well, the weight should never be so great that you can't carry it easily yourself. It is helpful to pack luggage wheels, which can be unfolded at airports. Some luggage comes with built-in wheels.

Always leave your name and address on the luggage itself, both inside and out. If you are spending a long time in any one country then also put your local address on all the luggage bags.

Pack any knives or scissors in your main suitcase and not in your carry-on luggage to avoid any embarrassment at security checks. Remember you are not allowed to carry knives of any kind on airplanes. I often travel with a utility knife that has a blade, scissors, can opener, spoon, fork, saw, and nail file in one. By mistake on one trip I packed it in my hand luggage. It was quickly taken away when security people checked our carry-on baggage at the airport.

Just before landing at our destination there was an announcement over the PA system: Would the person with the confiscated knife please press the call button to get the flight attendant's attention. You can imagine my embarrassment when all the passengers in the aircraft turned to look at Bonnie and me as if we were terrorists caught before we had a chance to hijack the plane.

Pack games or books that wile away the hours during long waits at airports. Sometimes we take a tiny chess and checkers game, a portable Scrabble set, and hand-held computer games for our children during the plane ride. Often there are games available from the flight attendant.

The most common mistake people make is packing too much. Remember to leave room in your bag for things you purchase on your holiday. You might want to pack a collapsible bag that does not take up much space but will expand to carry souvenirs and other purchases at the end of your vacation.

Here is a rough list of what you might want to pack for a two-week holiday:

MEN

Shoes
- thongs or flip-flops for the beach, which can also be used as slippers
- leather sandals for warm climates only
- firm leather or crepe-soled walking shoes that could be used for dress-up occasions

Socks
- 6 pair light and 1 or 2 heavy wool ones for cold weather

Pants
-shorts (2)
-jeans (1)
- 2 dress pants, one for casual wear and airports and one for formal dress-up situations
-underpants (4)
- bathing suits (2)

Shirts
-1 long-sleeved dress shirt
-1 short-sleeved dress shirt
-2 short- or long-sleeved casual shirts
-3 T-shirts of assorted colours

2 pyjamas (if you wear them)
1 sweater
1 belt to fit all pants
1 hat (for the sun) and a jacket to match the season

WOMEN

Shoes
-thongs or flip-flops
-leather sandals
-firm walking shoes (leather- or crepe-soled shoes that will go well with pants or skirts)
Socks
-2 pair panty hose (optional)
-light-weight socks (4 pair)
Pants
-2 shorts (one casual, one dress)
-dress slacks (1)
-jeans (1)
1 skirt with 2 matching tops that could be worn separately with shorts or slacks
1 fancy dress and 1 sun dress, if necessary
2 pyjamas
4 bras and 6 panties
2 bathing suits
1 raincoat easily folded into a small packet
1 fold-up umbrella, if required
1 sweater
1 jacket to match the season, if necessary
makeup/toiletry kit
1 hat or scarf (especially for holy places and for the sun)

CHILDREN (Under 3 years old)

enough disposable diapers to last at least 2 weeks or 6
cloth diapers with rubber pants or 6 pairs of underpants
diaper wet wipes in a container
4 shorts
4 matching tops (long- and short-sleeved)
2 jeans
1 dress pants
2 dresses for girls
2 sweat suits for warmth
2 pajamas (more if not toilet trained)
5 pair socks
1 sweater
1 coat
2 pair of shoes
2 bathing suits
1 sun hat
car seat (optional)
1 stroller for children under 4 who are poor walkers
6 plastic baby bottles and 6 nipples for infants
3 small compact toys and 4 books

I am not in favour of stuffed animals or blankets that children
can become dependent on. These create a big problem if they
are inadvertently left behind. If your child already has a security blanket or favorite transitional object then you can use the
vacation to break their dependence by leaving it behind and
dealing with the consequences.

CARRY-ON LUGGAGE

I recommend a piece of carry-on hand luggage that is durable, has multiple compartments and can fit under any airline seat. Inside this bag keep the following:

- small cosmetic zipper bag with a bar of soap in a plastic soap container, toothbrush, toothpaste and dental floss, razor with disposable razor blades and shaving cream
- shampoo
- bug repellent and sun block
- nail clipper and file
- hairbrush or comb
- cold-water laundry detergent
- small roll of toilet paper
- diary or writing book and pens
- books to read
-camera and film
-medications

Remember to wrap anything with liquid in a plastic bag. That way if it spills it won't ruin your luggage or anything in it. Carry at least one roll of toilet paper on you at all times and have a spare in your suitcase. It's amazing how many times you will be in a washroom that doesn't have toilet paper. Indeed, in many countries toilet paper is not used at all and only water in a bucket may be provided for you. Toilet paper can also serve as napkins, facial tissue, and even writing paper.

MEDICAL KIT

- adhesive bandages (25)
- roll of one-inch, white adhesive tape
- 2 x 2-inch sterile gauze pads (5)
- codeine for serious pain (20 tablets)
- Lomotil or Imodium for severe diarrhea (30 tablets)
- broad spectrum antibiotic like ciprofloxan for skin, urinary, chest or intestinal infections (one-week supply)
- ASA or Acetaminophen (50 tablets), liquid acetaminophen for infants
- antimalarial pills, where appropriate
- Halazone tablets or other water-sterilizing tablets
- water purifying cup made of iodine resin that sterilizes water as you pour through it
- birth-control pills, condoms, foam, diaphragm or other contraception
- medicine for specific health problems or drugs recommended by your physician

BOIL IT, BOTTLE IT, PEEL IT, COOK IT…
OR FORGET IT!

Some people do not like traveling because of the risk of getting sick. Every time they go away they become ill and land up in the hospital. They have to spend a week when they get home recuperating from the holiday. I could write another book about holiday disasters but I am trying to encourage travel not frighten you to death. I strongly recommend getting immunization, health insurance and medical travel advice before leaving home.

Some of the things that get people into problems are so called common sense issues. Unfortunately common sense is not common anymore. For example, drinking and driving; drinking unclean tap water; not using sun protection; walking barefoot in infected areas and traveling to areas where there are dangerous situations are fairly obvious activities to be avoided. Other things like taking prophylactic antibiotics, traveling with health problems, or preparing yourself for altitude sickness requires that you visit a doctor for proper medical guidance. The risk of getting sick depends on where you are going, for how long you will be staying and under what conditions. Traveling to India poses different risks than climbing Mt. Kilimanjaro.

Since there is an increased risk of getting infections in the Tropics and third world countries, you must take extra special care in avoiding undercooked or raw eggs, meat, poultry, or seafood. Stay away from fountain drinks, ice cubes or unpasteurized dairy products. Generally avoid fresh salads or fruit unless you peel them yourself because they could have been washed in unclean water. Remember, "travel expands the mind...and loosens the bowels."

Unprotected sex is extremely risky behaviour because of the threat of AIDS, hepatitis B, and other sexually transmitted diseases. But exposure to body fluids might occur from tattooing, acupuncture, body piercing and using shared razors. If you do get sick traveling abroad then you run the danger of being exposed to medical care that may not be up to standards and sometimes hazardous.

There is controversy by some people who believe that immunization is risky and causes great harm. They advocate not immunizing children and even refuse to immunize themselves.

Physicians fear that this could lead to an outbreak of childhood diseases like polio, whooping cough and measles.

I believe that immunization is one of the most important preventive weapons that modern health care possesses to stop the spread of disease. If all the nations of the world were committed to end suffering as a real priority then we would utilize our resources to feed everyone adequately and immunize the people of developing countries against deadly preventable diseases.

I suggest before traveling that families should bring their children's immunization up to date with respect to tetanus, diphtheria, polio, pertussis, hemophilus influenza, measles, mumps and rubella. All adults should get tetanus diphtheria shots every ten years.

Visit your doctor to find out if you need hepatitis A and B, meningitis, encephalitis, typhoid, pneumonia, influenza, rabies, cholera or yellow fever vaccines.

It is also important to find out if malaria is a risk and what precautions and pills to take. Malaria is a life-threatening infection and a number of vacationers coming home from tropical travel are dying from it every year. Risks and diseases change from year to year and what was appropriate for one country last year may not fit this year. Besides taking the proper prophylactic antibiotics, it is also important to use DEET mosquito repellents, sleep under treated mosquito nets, and stay covered up especially at night when the malaria (Anopheles) mosquitoes bite. If you are traveling to a malaria-endemic area and develop a fever while you are away or upon your return home maybe that you have malaria and should seek medical care immediately.

Tuberculosis is widespread in low-income countries.

Getting a TB skin test before and after traveling can determine if you have been in contact with TB. Travelers who plan to work in health disciplines or spend a long time in areas where TB is prevalent should consult their MD's about getting the BCG vaccine.

Probably the most common cause of death while away is heart disease. You should not travel if you have had a recent heart attack, have unstable angina, a serious irregular heart beat, or have uncontrolled congestive heart failure. If you do have heart disease I recommend that you travel with a copy of your most recent ECG and a letter from your doctor describing your condition and medication. People who have shortness of breath at rest, pneumonia, or poorly controlled asthma are also advised not to take the risk of going away until their condition is better controlled. Some travelers with serious lung problems may have to be prescribed oxygen during the flight.

Diabetics must carefully plan meal arrangements, snacks, and how you will transport your insulin. You should be ready for long delays on airlines and carry extra food, medications and glucagon. These items should be kept in carry-on bags, not in checked luggage. You should monitor your blood sugar closely on holiday. The role of the sun in more rapid absorption of insulin needs to be remembered. A Medic-Alert bracelet is also recommended.

Food allergies can also be a problem in countries where English is not understood. Carrying pictures of the ingredients or food to be avoided could help, but is no guarantee that the meal will be safe. If you have a peanut or shellfish allergy then you must be extremely careful because many of the ingredients may contain allergic triggers and the waiter and cook may not even know about it. Many airlines are now banning peanuts on

89

their flights, but they cannot control what passengers bring. Therefore it is important to carry injectable adrenalin plus an antihistamine along with you at all times. Similarly if you have a bee sting allergy that is life threatening carrying adrenalin when you are going to risky areas is advisable.

Certain precautions need to be taken if you have an immune deficiency disorder. You are at higher risk for developing infections and likely respond poorly to vaccines. It is inadvisable to get live vaccines like yellow fever, oral polio or typhoid, measles, mumps and rubella, chickenpox or BCG. It is recommended to be immunized against influenza, pneumonia and all other inactivated vaccines where appropriate. Your physician may want to give you passive immunization with specific immunoglobulins or prescribe preventive medications.

Obviously if you do get sick while you are away, seek qualified medical advice. Similarly, if after you return home you are not well or if you got sick during your holiday then visit your family physician so he or she can assess your condition and give appropriate treatment.

Medical science has been making great strides with respect to prevention and it is important to get up to date information. It is far better to prevent problems from happening than to try to fix something afterward. A milligram of prevention is worth a kilogram of cure.

SAY CHEESE

Photographs are not only a wonderful way to remember your holidays but they provide you with a personal thank-you to send to friends and acquaintances you met during your holiday. First you have to decide what camera to take, whether to take slides or prints, where to get your film developed and what to do at airport security. I would like to share a few important pointers to help you capture your holidays forever.

Is your next vacation spot a photographer's paradise or is it a place where you will just be taking photos primarily of people and events? If you will be seeing spectacular scenery then you'll want a 35 mm camera with a telephoto, wide angle or other special lens. However, if you know little about photography and just want to have the memories, then take a compact, fully automatic camera that easily fits into a purse or pocket. The camera should have a clear viewfinder, be simple to use, and have a built-in flash. You'll use 100 ASA film for the majority of your shots but it's also helpful to have some 400 ASA film for darker indoor situations.

SLIDES OR PRINTS?

Then you need to decide whether to take colour prints or slides. Many people take slides because the quality of the photo on a big screen far surpasses what can be gotten from a print. The three-dimensional look, the depth of colour and the fine detail can't be matched. You can also show the slides to more than one person at a time and you can explain your vacation to many people rather than having to put your prints into an album and explain each photo individually. Colour slides are also less expensive than prints.

But with prints you don't have to take out a projector or movie screen each time you want to show your photos. Also you can make copies and blow-ups of your favourite shots without sacrificing detail. Blow-ups of slides will not usually be the same quality as prints.

91

We always take prints and put them into photo albums separated according to trips or countries. Then when we go over to someone's house to talk about our trip, we can take the album along. We also like to make blow-ups of our favourite shots. We have taken our best photos and enlarged them to 8 x 10", 11 x 14" and even 16 x 20".

The walls in our study are covered with photos, so when we walk by we are continually reminded of our holidays. It triggers pleasant memories. In addition, we have photo albums with 8 x 10" blow-ups of our favourite shots.

If you have taken a roll of film that has many shots of people on it and you were intending to send copies to these individuals it is easier to pay a small amount for duplicates when you first develop the film rather than having to go back and make copies later. Sometimes it is easier just to take two shots of the same scene and send one to your host or friend.

Bonnie and I have developed a photo policy. We pack enough film so that we never have to worry about running out. On long trips we restock our supply in large cities like Hong Kong or Singapore where film is inexpensive. If either of us decides to take a photo the other person doesn't interfere. We don't limit each other and rarely offer our advice about how to take the shot. This has avoided the petty bickering that was more common on our earlier vacations when both film and money was scarce.

DEVELOPING FILM

Develop your prints at reliable places while traveling. This gives you instant feedback about how you're doing as a photographer. If you have a new camera, then it is imperative to develop your film right away to learn how to improve your technique. It is also safer to develop the films than to carry undeveloped film on long journeys.

If we are away for an extended trip, we will often send developed photos home for our families to see and share in our vacation. We send the negatives home in a separate package, so if one package got lost we still have the other. Some people send undeveloped film home for relatives to develop. However, I'm always afraid that the mail could be x-rayed spoiling the film or the precious film could be lost. If you are on a short vacation then keeping undeveloped film with you in your carry-on luggage is simplest. But don't leave film in your luggage if there is any risk of theft. Sometimes it is even worth storing it in the safety deposit box of your hotel or leaving it outside your bags in the hotel room in case your bags get stolen.

If you are going on a long journey or are taking many photos it is helpful to make a list of all your shots describing the places and people that you've photographed. This avoids the dilemma of trying to remember what the photos were about months later.

Even though security officials at the airport often say the surveillance equipment they use is safe for film, because we are cautious, we separate all undeveloped film and our camera from our bags and let the security officers check them by hand. Be prepared to be asked by security officers to take a photo with your camera to prove that your camera isn't a gun. We always ask the guard to take our picture rather than waste a shot altogether.

VIDEO?

Sometimes on short holidays we take a video camera along to capture the sight and sounds of our vacation. But on longer trips the video camera is an intrusion and it alters the spirit of the trip. I would find myself worrying more about the camera than enjoying what it is I'm taping.

I've watched tourists spend their whole time organizing everybody and everything around a camera — whether video or photographic. They think they are Steven Spielberg and become so busy with the "shot" they fail to appreciate what's happening right in from of them. They end up seeing their holiday through the camera lens instead of their own lens.

I'm sure you've seen people arguing over whether to take a photo? The wife starts snapping a shot and her partner says, "No, not that!" He snaps at her to take a different shot, and gripes that she's wasting film. A battle over who controls the camera follows.

I know one couple that took a movie camera along on a three-month journey. There were so many arguments about when and how to take shots, the husband became resentful and when they returned home he never bothered to splice together the 20 rolls he took. In this way he got back at his wife for her controlling behaviour.

If you can avoid the obsession for perfection and just secure the movement and sound of your trip, then seeing your vacation in motion is a special way of capturing the memory.

DIGITAL PHOTOGRAPHY

At the time of writing this book digital photography is becoming popular and is transforming photography as we know it. With a digital camera, a personal computer, photo software package and a scanner you can create images beyond anything you have ever imagined. No more taking your film to the store; waiting for your developing; having to go back to make copies or blowups. Now you can take your shots, and view them on the screen attached to the camera, eliminating the images you don't like and keeping the ones that are just right.

Then you can go immediately to your computer or even TV and see them on the screen. You can edit, crop, enlarge, and print your own photos or send them, via the internet to the photo developing store where they can print them for you.

Another option is to post them on a web page and let your friends and relatives visit via the internet and view them at their leisure. Or you can email the photos during your vacation.

Another advantage is that the photos can be filed and stored on your hard drive or disc and you can easily search for them in the future. You can even take your existing old photos, scan them into your computer and digitize them as well.

There are cameras that combine both video and still photography eliminating the worry about carrying so much equipment. You can view your stills and videos and edit them on your computer or TV. Soon there will be systems available with chair modules to experience a vacation in virtual reality replicating the sounds, sights, and movement of being away.

Digital photography is changing the way we view images and once the limiting factor of cost is overcome then digital will be the way to go.

PHOTO ETIQUETTE

It's important to realize that the inhabitants of some countries do not like to have their photos taken. Sometimes this is for religious reasons: they believe if you take their photo you are robbing their spirit. They can get quite angry and even try to take your camera away. So it is important to ask about photos before you start snapping away and get permission from your subjects. For example, you are not allowed to take photos of the Masai Mara tribe of Kenya. On the other hand, many people of poorer countries like India, Morocco and Thailand would like to be paid something for being photographed. It is appropriate to pay a modest amount when asked. I have met many photographers of high integrity who always ask permission first before taking photos of people. They would never take sneak shots and run away.

When we were in Thailand, Michael, a U.S. sailor, took black and white shots of the natives, got the film developed immediately at a local photo store and went back the next day and distributed the pictures to the people he photographed. Needless to say, he was very popular. It was a wonderful way to spread goodwill and get to know the people of the country. Some people take a Polaroid camera for that purpose and give out a photo while taking another for themselves on their 35 mm camera. They find they get great cooperation for poses when people know they will get a photo as a reward.

In many countries photos are not allowed to be taken in airports, military outposts or holy places. We have seen tourists who have had their film taken away from them because they inadvertently took photos in a restricted area.

Photos are a wonderful way to capture your vacation forever. They are a precious memento of your holiday. With the right camera, the proper film, a relaxed attitude and putting your photos immediately into albums, you'll have hours and hours of pleasure reliving a special holiday long after its over. A photo is worth a thousand words.

STICK 'EM UP

Nothing spoils a vacation like being robbed. Most of the time theft is preventable if you follow a few basic principles. Usually when traveling you will carry cash both in the currency of your host country, as well as from home. Most of your money will likely be in travelers' cheques but you will also have credit cards, as well as important papers such as a passport, an airplane ticket, a birth certificate, and a driver's license. Sometimes you may have jewellery, a camera, exposed film, a notebook computer, a diary and an address book.

Your money and valuables are safer on you than left in your hotel room or in your luggage unless there is a secure place, such as a hotel safe, that can guarantee the safety of your valuables. Keep most of your eggs in one basket and take good care of that basket. But in case you lose these eggs, it's wise to have an emergency cache. Develop a sixth sense about where you are carrying your valuables especially in crowded streets or busy tourist sites. Beware of strangers intruding too closely into your personal space.

Men should carry travelers' cheques, cash and credit cards in their front pockets and walk with their hand down touching that most important pocket. I usually put my wallet in my right front pants pocket and loose change and cash in my left front pants pocket. If there is no room left in the front pockets I will carry my travelers' cheques in my back pocket.

Remember it's fairly easy for a professional pickpocket to lift a wallet from your back pocket.

If you are a woman, are not carrying a bag, and are traveling alone, I'd recommend you get a false pocket made for the inside of your jacket and inside the front of your pants. Here you can put your passport and airline tickets. A cotton money belt, which can be worn around your waist and under your clothes, is also a good place to tuck your valuables. Since it's worn inside your clothes it's difficult for a robber to reach it. Since it's cotton, it is lightweight, can be washed and doesn't sweat too much. In some countries you can buy a regular man's belt that has a hidden zipper on the inside. You can hide hundred dollar bills in the belt as a last resort in case everything else is stolen.

It's not uncommon for tourists to lose their valuables while sunning on a beach. I have met quite a few people who went swimming only to return to find their clothes, camera and money stolen. On a remote beach in southern Thailand, two young people met and fell instantly into limerance. In a moment of passion they ripped off their clothes and jumped into the ocean. They were so enthralled by each other and the romantic setting that they failed to notice someone sneaking off with everything they owned. We knew they were embarking on an adventure, as we saw them standing naked wrapped in someone else's towels describing the theft to the police.

PURSE PROBLEMS

If you a carry a purse or a handbag it is a good place to keep your valuables. However, they can be stolen. In some countries razor blades are used to cut through your purse to the goods inside. A purse with inside pockets or compartments can help prevent this. Other thieves may cut the strap and snatch the entire purse. Occasionally robbers will work in pairs. One bumps into you or distracts you, while the other picks your purse from the other side. While standing on the side of the road in Bali, Indonesia a good friend of mine had his valuable pouch ripped out of his hand by a man on a motorcycle. The motorcycle was gone before everyone had a chance to realize what had happened. Another trick is for the thief to grab your purse while you are getting on a bus or subway then jump off leaving you behind empty handed.

Be cautious when you are stopped on the street and asked for change. When you take out your money to be a good Samaritan, the thief can grab your purse and take off. I've heard of a similar trick when trying to change money on the black market. When you hand over the money to be exchanged, the thief just takes your money and runs.

Make sure that you keep the open side of your purse facing inward or toward your body. It helps to have a strap or buckle over the opening as well. Bonnie once had someone reach in and take out her wallet while she was at a cashier, paying for some merchandise. She didn't realize the money was gone until she reached the next store and went to pay for something else.

DA RULES

If you are traveling with another person you can divide and conquer. One of you should carry the handbag or purse with the passports, airplane tickets and travelers' cheques. The other can carry the hard cash, the credit cards and the camera. Record all the numbers of the plane tickets, travelers' cheques, credit cards and passports and have a copy in each bag, as well as an extra copy tucked aside elsewhere and one back home.

Lately I have been charging everything possible to my VISA credit card that gives air miles or travel points for every dollar spent. In this way I can get free tickets when I have accumulated enough points. This also puts off paying for everything immediately and enables me to pay for the cost of the trip upon my return.

Carry most of your money in the form of travelers' cheques because they can always be replaced. You can carry the entire amount right from the beginning of your trip or if you are traveling for three months or longer you can get an American Express credit card and pick up travelers' cheques at American Express offices as you go. Some people have money wired to various banks along their journey, but this can be a hassle and often the exchange rate is poor.

In many countries it's better not to exchange a lot of money at the airport or at hotels because they usually offer the poorest rate of exchange. It often pays to shop around at various banks to see who has the best rates that day before exchanging large sums. Be extremely careful about going to an exchange booth that offers a great rate but then adds a huge service charge. Always ask about commissions or extras first before you sign any travelers' cheques.

Sometimes merchants will give you a better exchange rate if you pay for something in American dollars. Generally it's best to carry small bills in a foreign currency. It's more convenient for buses, taxis, and bartering.

PRECIOUS POSSESSIONS

Often your most important possessions are your address book, diary and laptop computer because what's in those things usually can't be replaced. When Bonnie and I travel we have an address book that contains the names of everyone we know in every country we visit. This is one possession that we cherish and never want to have stolen.

To prevent theft keep your diary, precious papers, and photos lying unpacked in your room rather than hiding them in your suitcase. If a thief does steal your luggage then at least your books or precious papers will be left scattered around the room. Since they probably have little value to a robber they are unlikely to be stolen. Of course, always back up your hard disc on your portable computer and keep the floppy discs in a place separate from your computer.

It is becoming more common to have baggage stolen at an airport, train or bus station. Getting your computer, handbag, and camera ripped off during the security check also happens. Be extra careful to keep a close eye on your possessions in these places.

Doing business in western and central Africa, Algeria, Colombia and certain politically sensitive places carries certain risks. When you are traveling on business, you may be dressed in a suit or fancy outfit, carrying an attaché case, traveling alone and looking wealthy. Therefore you are more likely to be targeted for petty crime or political gain.

Don't travel with diamonds and expensive jewellery, especially in poorer countries. It's just too tempting for locals who are just barely surviving. You can also reduce your chances of getting robbed by dressing down, blending in with the local dress and not appearing too flashy.

Vacations are pleasurable times but being robbed can be a disaster. If you follow some of this advice, then you can help prevent the disappearance of your money or your material possessions. A little bit of paranoia goes a long way to preventing theft. Remember, trust no one except your mother.

FOR RENT

If you are going away for a week or two then it is important to have some responsible person check your home every few days. Most insurance policies stipulate that the place cannot be totally unattended for 48 hours or the insurance will not cover damages like burst pipes, burglary or fire.

Homes can be burglarized when unattended even for a few hours, but if there is no one home for many days, weeks or months, the chances of being robbed increase. There are clues that alert robbers to vacant premises. If your grass is not cut, the snow not shovelled, newspapers or handbills not cleared away, the mail not taken inside and the lights not coming on and off it, signals would-be robbers that no one is at home.

Have a trusted neighbour visit daily to collect mail and circulars and turn different lights on in the house. Some people use timers to turn lights on and off at various intervals. There are also sophisticated systems that operate via a mini computer, so that all the lights inside and out can be placed on a timing circuit that mimics a normal pattern of turning lights on and off.

If you have an apartment or home and you are going away for more than a few months, you may be able to sublet or rent it during your absence. This will help cover some of your expenses and you will have someone taking care of things and checking your property.

Unfortunately, sometimes the people renting your premises can also wreak havoc and there are many sad stories of thousands of dollars of damage done to places left by trusting lessors. You want to find someone who is in some way compatible with your lifestyle. If you can't interview the people, then at least get appropriate references and check them thoroughly.

It's important to draw up a legal agreement with your lawyer. Be sure to have a contract stipulating any restrictions. You should also have a security deposit that you can return once you're certain everything is in good condition. Your tenant should be responsible for breakage, damage and maintenance. As well, you may wish to include clauses about smoking and pets. Be aware of long-distance phone calls, and do not return the security deposit until you have checked with the phone company about long-distance charges while you were away.

Write down a list of names and phone numbers of trades like electricians, plumbers, lawyers, and gardeners who you use and trust. Provide the person who is taking care of your place with this list so, if necessary, they can call responsible people who will do a good job.

Some travelers who rent out their premises leave it empty or prefer to take their expensive household items like VCRs, cameras, silverware, furs and art and store them with a friend or relative who can look after them. When we rented our house for nine months, our tenants didn't want our art on the wall because they had their own pieces they wanted to display. We left some valuables with different relatives and also picked one room in our house to lock all our personal, irreplaceable items.

Sometimes it may be necessary to store your furniture with a storage company or warehouse for a monthly fee. The main point to remember is not to leave anything in your home that you would hate to see lost, damaged or stolen. During our 14 month sabbatical, we gave one car to my sister-in-law to drive and stored another at my in-law's house. We asked them to drive it around the block every now and again to keep it in running order. Since we were gone for such a long time we gave up our apartment and had to store our possessions with friends and relatives. We itemized all our worldly goods in a book and kept track of where we had stored them. When we returned, we slowly re-acquired all our things.

Who would want to rent out your place for a few months? There are invariably people who will be visiting your city for a short time on business or for pleasure. Sometimes people who are moving need a place to stay while their home or apartment is being built or vacated. Occasionally corporations need accommodations for their employees for a few months while long-term housing is located. Also, some families will exchange their home with another family in a different city or country.

How do you find someone to rent your home? You can place an ad in the daily paper or even in a newspaper in another city. Register with a large commercial real estate firm that has contacts worldwide. Contact large, international companies in your neighbourhood who may be hosting out-of-town staff. There are agencies that specialize in house swapping or finding short-term tenants. Ask your friends and acquaintances if they know of anyone wanting to rent your place while you are away.

PRECAUTIONS

If you have business affairs and decisions to be made about money, it can be helpful to go to a lawyer and have a power of attorney drawn up. This will give authority to your closest, most trustworthy representative to act legally on your behalf while you're away. But remember, this gives someone else complete power over all your possessions. You wouldn't want to come home to find your house sold and your bank account cleaned out. While you're at your lawyer's take a few minutes to make out a will. This will ensure your wishes will be followed to the letter in the event of your untimely death.

If you are gone for an extended period of time, then have the person responsible for keeping tabs on your affairs be sure to open your mail, pay all bills and respond to any urgent matters on your behalf. This person could also send you your mail to pre-arranged addresses so you can keep up with what's been happening back home.

DELIVER D-LETTER DA SOONER DA BETTER

It's a warm and special feeling to be thousands of miles away from home in a strange land, hearing only foreign tongues and open a letter from a friend or family member with news from the old neighbourhood.

If you are away for a long time and you want to get mail from home consider the following. First, decide where you can receive your mail and photocopy a page or two of all the addresses where you will pick up your mail. Distribute these to everyone you know. Second, take with you the addresses of all the people you want to keep in touch with. Then write people to tell them where you are and where you will be next, including estimated arrival and departure dates and addresses. Our practice was to write everyone once and then write back to everyone who wrote us.

Canada and some other countries are fortunate to have their embassies abroad receive and keep mail on their behalf. In most countries therefore, we chose to receive mail care of the Canadian embassy. This was ideal because we could go to our embassy and tell the officials where we were going. We picked up our mail, used the toilet, drank safe water, read a few magazines to discover what we were not missing at home, and received instructions from embassy officials about specific dangers or problems that existed where we were going to next. For example, while in Australia we learned there was an outbreak of cholera in Bali. While in Thailand in 1975 we were warned not to go to Laos because there were anti-U.S. demonstrations and it was too dangerous.

Many embassies, such as those of the U.S. will not hold mail for their citizens, so alternatives need to be arranged. Then, of course, some cities do not have an embassy. When we were in a city like Denpasar, or Katmandu that had no Canadian embassy, we had our mail sent to us via the American Express office. This worked well but a few things should be kept in mind. The mail is distributed only to certain locations so when you are copying out addresses make sure the office you choose provides mail service. There are also certain times when mail is handed out and long line-ups are not unusual. If you do not carry American Express Travelers Cheques or an American Express Card, then there can be a charge for the letters you receive. Finally, it can be a long trek to get to the offices in cities like Katmandu and Denpasar.

You can have your mail sent to the Post Restante or General Delivery at a city's main post office. Or, if you have pre-arranged reservations at hotels and you know the date of your arrival then people could write to you care of the hotel. They should write on the envelope " hold for arrival " along with the date when you expect to be there. Then when you check in the letters will be waiting and you don't have to go on a long jaunt across town to retrieve your mail. If you have friends or relatives you plan to visit mail can always be sent there. Any urgent messages can also be sent to these addresses via telegram.

You may wish to ask the people you write to save your letters and postcards. This can be a wonderful record of your trip to reminisce over when you return home.

E-MAIL

E-mail has really taken over as the medium in which to communicate to people back home. Occasionally it is difficult to find a service provider in developing countries. But usually there are Internet cafes and business offices everywhere where you can go on-line and connect up to your Internet service provider very cheaply. Many people use free E-mail providers like Hotmail and communicate with other travelers wherever they go. In this way they can arrange to meet people and find out the latest up-to-date information as they are traveling. You can even arrange for accommodation, tickets, weather reports and other services before you get to your destination.

E-mail also allows many business people to stay in touch with their offices when they are away. It is easy to carry a laptop computer which has a modem and be able to connect up to the world wide web anywhere there is a telephone.

Remember to get the correct plug attachment for your computer, because there are different wall sockets in countries like China and Indonesia that do not fit North American or European standards.

In the first half of the book I have tried to explain why holidays are good for you. In the upcoming chapters I will share some of my personal travel stories and lessons I have learned while being away. The second half of the book is meant to whet your travel appetites. As you read about different journeys, you will be reminded of times and experiences of your own. I find that when I hear travel stories I get itchy feet and want to head out on the road again.

PART TWO

CHAPTER EIGHT
ENJOY YOUR FLIGHT

This is your captain speaking. Welcome to Go Away Airlines. Our flying time will be 178 more pages. We will be traveling through the South Pacific, to Kenya, Indonesia, India, Afghanistan, China and Taiwan and returning via Algonquin Park.

Please keep your seats in the upright position, tray tables up and seatbelts securely fastened. I will now review the safety features of this book.

You will always have your life jacket under your seat, emergency exits at the front and back cover. In the unlikely event of an emergency you can put the book over your head, to protect you from the elements. Please remove your shoes when gliding through this book.

In the event of too much hot air in the text, the oxygen mask will automatically come down. Pull it towards your mouth and breathe normally. If you are traveling with young children, first put on your mask before attending to your child.

It is always advisable to keep your seatbelts fastened throughout this book. There is no smoking aboard this flight or in the lavatories. Anyone found smoking or tampering with the smoke detectors will be at risk of imprisonment or a fine of $100,000.

Sit back and enjoy the journey. Thank you for choosing Go Away Airlines. I hope you will choose to pick up this book at some future date and come travel with me again.

I WANT TO INFECT YOU WITH THE TRAVEL BUG

I have a wanderlust and curiosity about the way people live in different parts of the world. I am a dreamer of places; I conjure up images of foreign destinations. When I leave the security of my home and the city I grew up in, I get in touch with my inner self and transcend time and space. When I'm on vacation I'm more creative, easygoing and fun loving.

Am I just a vagabond addicted to new sights and sounds? I do know that I am happiest when I'm away from home. It's not that home is bad, but the excitement of new cultures, spiritual places and people who see the world in entirely different ways inspires me. We all see and interpret events from a unique perspective. We might share common experiences yet each one of us has our own slant on things. It's the slant that fascinates me.

I've been extremely lucky to be able to travel and capture my experiences in print and in photographs. Usually when I return from a journey, my friends and patients ask me questions about where I've been and what I've done. In 1981 I began to document my memories in the form of travel writing. Derek Cassels, the former editor of The Medical Post, encouraged me to send him articles about my trips, which he subsequently published under the heading of "Doctor on the Wing". People who read these stories seemed to enjoy them and so I began a career in travel writing that has brought me lots of joy, as well as a way to record my thoughts, feelings and visual images of my time away.

I wrote a series of articles from 1981 to 1998. There are common themes that keep emerging. Some of the articles are about traditional healing. I found highly evolved systems of healing in India and China that were developed thousands of years ago. I had an opportunity to interview herbalists, bone-setters and spiritual healers. These folk healers are dying and not being replaced. I wanted to talk about them and their traditions with the idea of preserving the knowledge that is rapidly disappearing.

Some of my articles are about places like Afghanistan, Kashmir and Yugoslavia that at the time of this publication were no longer tourist destinations because of political unrest. I wanted to let people know how special these places are and how rapidly religious differences and politics can destroy a country.

A number of articles are about foreign cultures and unfold like a travelogue. By reading about these places, people and customs I hope readers would gain a better understanding of the peoples of the world. Once you know their history and traditions their way of life doesn't seem so foreign anymore.

The world is ever changing. This is a fact of nature. As I get older, I long to hold on to things the way they were. But I've learned that eco-tourism is an oxymoron. The very fact that humans enter a region transforms it. I returned to places only to find the most precious natural resources destroyed. I've mourned beautiful forests with ancient trees cut down to fuel the insatiable desire for wood. I've seen coral reefs teaming with fish completely dead only a few years later. Sleepy towns and isolated beaches have been taken over by foreign investors and crammed with hotels, shops and restaurants.

Why shouldn't this happen? Why shouldn't impoverished areas benefit from an influx of tourist dollars? Why shouldn't so-called primitive people benefit from the computer age? It's easy to be self-righteous and criticize. I realize that I am no different. If I had a chance, I would probably take over some underdeveloped area and cut down the trees if I thought I could make my fortune.

Travel writing for me is very personal. Readers get to see the world as filtered through my eyes. I tell stories, give opinions, and provide information that reflects my view of the world around me. My goal is to stimulate you to dream your next holiday. I want to fuel the craving you have to go away and see what's going on in your neighbour's backyard.

People from every part of the world share a common humanity. Kindness, hospitality and smiles cross all boundaries of race, religion, politics and culture. The world is full of the most beautiful mountains, beaches, sunsets and trees. I hope by reading this collection of travel stories that you will call up your travel agent and plan to visit our planet. The world is desperately in need of messengers of peace and goodwill.

Don't leave home without tolerance, love and generosity, not only for the people but the flora and fauna of this great world we live in.

CHAPTER NINE
EASTERN EXPERIENCES FOR A WESTERN BRAIN

BITTEN BY THE BUG

Doctor David Adamson, a classmate of mine at the University of Toronto, is the person responsible for lighting my travel spark. One day, in 1972 while we were in medical school he began talking about his trip around the world. He invited Bonnie and me over to his apartment to see the slides of his journey. We were immediately hooked.

His incredible photos and exciting tales captured our imagination. Visions of trekking in Nepal, exploring the outback of Australia, winding through India and temple hopping in Thailand danced in our brains. It was as if our unconscious minds were mesmerized and a post-hypnotic suggestion was implanted in our heads. That evening we vowed to take a year off from the "rat race" and travel around the world. If David Adamson, could do it then surely we could too. We put aside our money for a dream.

After a few more rigorous years of medical school and a gruelling internship, I felt depleted. On July 10, 1974, Bonnie and I packed up our apartment, and said goodbye to relatives, friends, material possessions and responsibilities. For almost 15 months we circled the globe. Our only regret was coming home too soon. One thing was certain: we would travel again. The travel bug had infected us and we didn't want to cure the disease.

It was during this first sabbatical I got introduced to complementary medicine, a subject that would later have a significant effect on my professional career.

Halfway through the 15-month trip I was living on a beautiful, hand-carved, wooden houseboat on Nagin Lake in Kashmir, Northern India with Jack, a dentist-psychotherapist from California and his wife Lynn. Jack woke up one morning with severe pain in his back. He had a history of a "tricky back" problem and every now and again it would go "out of position" and he would have his chiropractor put it back in place.

I had just finished my medical training and internship and thought that I knew everything about medicine. I was at the pinnacle of my knowledge and capabilities. But for Jack's back problem, I could do nothing. In medical school I had learned about bed rest, analgesics, muscle relaxants and physiotherapy, but in Kashmir there was none of this. I had only rest to offer him.

Jack would have nothing to do with rest. In desperation, he lay down on the handmade Indian carpet of the houseboat and got himself into the position he usually got into for his chiropractor. He tried to show me where to put my hands and in what direction to apply force, but I just couldn't get it right. I felt helpless and inadequate.

We asked our friendly houseboat owner, Ali, for his advice. He suggested we seek out the local healer. I decided to go along as spy and protector because I was nervous for my friend. We traveled by horse and buggy four kilometers to a small town called Hazratbal on the outskirts of Srinagar. After arriving in the village, we asked where we might find the local healer. We were led to a distant sidewalk and there on the curb sat a short, 5' 2", grey-haired man surrounded by a crowd of some 20 people.

Of course we stood out like sore thumbs and when the

healer saw Jack, who was 6' 4", he motioned for him to step forward. In sign language he asked my friend what was wrong. Jack pointed to his back and made a few grunts using the international language of groans. The healer stood up, turned Jack around in front of him, put his knee in the middle of Jack's back, lifted him off the ground, produced a "crunching" sound, and dropped him back on his feet.

Within a few seconds, Jack was completely cured. The pain was gone. I was impressed. I realized there was more to learn about healing than I had been taught in medical school. There were people who possessed knowledge and skills passed down from one generation to another. Modern medicine didn't have all the answers.

Another incident had a profound effect on the way I perceived healing. During that same sabbatical I was staying in Hong Kong with Dr. Andy Wong, a friend from medical school. Andy never showed any interest in traditional medicine when we interned together in Toronto. He seemed like a very conservative, down-to-earth doctor. But while doing his internal medicine training in Hong Kong he became interested in acupuncture. He did a demonstration for Bonnie and me, showing us how the point finder attached to his acupuncture machine could identify problems in the body just by scanning the external ear.

He explained that the whole body was mapped out in the ear and that every point on the ear corresponded to an area of the body or its organ. If he touched an area of the ear with the probe and the machine made a high-pitched sound then that suggested there was something wrong with that organ. I was sceptical.

When he touched my ear there seemed to be nothing

117

wrong. Yet when he touched Bonnie's ear with the point find-er, a loud buzz was emitted. He was touching the kidney area of her ear and sure enough Bonnie had a history of kidney and bladder infections. When Andy touched the lung area of his own ear the lung area was sensitive. He thought this was because as a child he had repeated bouts of bronchitis. Twenty months later we got the tragic news that, at the age of 29, Andy had developed cancer of the lung and died. The acupuncture machine had detected something long before it showed up on an x-ray taken around the same time.

Was it just coincidental that a problem could be detected by an acupuncture machine point finder before it was seen on an x-ray? The incident with the local Kashmiri healer and the introduction to acupuncture stimulated my curiosity. I began looking at alternative ways of healing. It has helped me keep an open mind and view things from the broadest perspective. When I returned to Toronto and started practicing medicine, I began to take many courses in acupuncture, orthopaedic manipulation and other healing modalities. By leaving home I became exposed to new and exciting concepts. I have a differ-ent slant on medicine and healing because I had a chance to leave my own backyard.

The longer journey had begun. My Western-trained med-ical mind had become awakened to the possibilities of Eastern healing.

CHAPTER TEN
OFF TO SEE THE WIZARDS

Five years, one child, one medical practice, one house and two cars later, we broke away again. Things were different this time. We were no longer young, starry-eyed idealists with no material possessions. We had become responsible, dependable members of the community. No longer could we pass ourselves off as helpless, poverty-stricken students bumming from one place to another.

Our three-year old son, Larry, brought us down to earth and forced us to appear more grounded and respectable. We even carried a stroller.

Saying goodbye and packing up this time was harder than in 1974. Handing over my medical practice, our house, our cars, our bank accounts and a newly published book made life a great deal more complicated than it had been five years before. By the time we left for Los Angeles in December 1980, two days after John Lennon was murdered, we were exhausted and stressed. Larry even had an ear infection and was on antibiotics. After a few days cocooned with friends in Los Angeles, we flew to hostile Tahiti.

LEAVING TAHITI

While hitchhiking in beautiful Tahiti we were picked up in an old army truck by a helpful Tahitian named Daniel. He told us to visit Rarotonga, the friendliest Island in the Pacific. After a few weeks in exquisite but heartless Tahiti, we longed for a friendly face. He lured us further by giving us the name of his cousin in Rarotonga whom he said would take care of us.

119

After hearing about the warm, welcoming people of Rarotonga a few more times, we went to the airline office to reroute our ticket. We needed an ongoing ticket and a hotel reservation to get permission to visit Rarotonga, so from Tahiti, we booked a night at the Turangi Motel, the only one that we could afford. We could travel to Fiji, our next destination via Rarotonga without affecting the price of our around-the-world airline ticket.

It was a little after 6:30 in the morning New Year's Day. Bonnie, little Larry and I were standing in front of the Hotel Tahiti waiting for the taxi to come and take us to the airport. The night before we had booked a cab because we were told there were no buses on New Year's Day. We began to worry that the taxi wouldn't come, doubting if the receptionist at the desk had really ordered it at all. We were afraid we'd be late for our flight so I said to the doorman, "We're going to stop Le Truck because our taxi is late."

Le Truck was the large, open-backed, old truck with wooden benches that served as the official public bus service for the island. It had already passed our Hotel on the way to the airport. Instead of paying $15 for the taxi, Le Truck would only cost us $1.50.

But the doorman, a huge, heavy-set, slightly drunk Tahitian, said to us in French,

"You ordered the taxi and you must wait for it."

Since it was already 10 minutes past the time the taxi was scheduled to come, I felt justified in moving my bags to the side of the road since I saw Le Truck coming in the far distance. The big, burly doorman, however, had other ideas and blocked my path. I tried to explain our predicament but he screamed at us, "You called for the taxi, you must wait for it."

"Get out of my way, we're taking Le Truck," I shouted back.

Then the doorman did the unexpected. He picked up my burgundy overnight bag and proceeded to walk back with it to the hotel. Dumbfounded, I told Bonnie to stop the bus and I chased after the doorman. He put my bag behind the receptionist's desk all the while yelling and screaming threats at me in French.

I scooted behind the front desk to retrieve my bag when a small, 5', thin unfriendly man, also reeking of alcohol, grabbed me by the collar and started shouting, "You wanna fight? You wanna fight?"

He was gesturing wildly with his hands and making what looked like karate chops. He was apparently the hotel's assistant manager.

Those two, half-drunk Tahitians started pushing and shoving me. I was frightened. At the same time I hoped they would not hurt a tourist. My thoughts were on just one thing — to get my bag and get on the bus. I grabbed my burgundy bag and pushed my way back to the road and the waiting Le Truck. Bonnie had by now put Larry on the bus along with half our luggage. A small crowd was beginning to gather.

The atmosphere was tense. The doorman was now screaming at the driver to take off with our son and leave us stranded. I was trying to climb onto the bus but he kept blocking my way. Bonnie was yelling, "My baby's on the bus, we have to get on."

Other people in the bus were yelling things in French but I wasn't sure whose side they were on. Then the manager joined the melee shrieking that I should wait for the taxi. Finally, however, we pushed past the big doorman and hopped onto Le Truck as it pulled away heading towards the airport. The driver had waited for us and I gratefully paid the 250 francs.

When we at last got on the Air New Zealand flight for Rarotonga, I felt exhilarated and alive. All my frustrations and anger at the Tahitians and their rudeness was exorcized by my yelling and pushing. The screaming and shoving had somehow released the tremendous tension that had built up in me over leaky showers, peeling wallpaper, broken televisions, snarky receptionists, excessive prices and the worm in my salad. I let out two weeks of resentment along with all the anxiety about leaving Toronto for this journey. I felt reborn.

Now the trip had really begun.

CHAPTER ELEVEN
COOKS ISLANDS – ARRIVAL AT LAST

The Cook Islands are a series of 15 islands spread out over 850,000 square miles of Pacific Ocean, just south of the Tropic of Capricorn. To the west lies Tonga and Samoa and to the east Tahiti. The largest, most-developed island, Rarotonga, is dominated by ancient peaks 2,000 meters high and ringed by a coral reef. The flora is wondrous: coconuts, hibiscus, gardenias, and bougainvilleas.

Captain James Cook explored most of the islands in 1786, although Captain Bligh visited Aitutaki shortly before the mutiny on the Bounty in 1792. There was intense missionary activity by John Wesley in 1826 and the majority of the islanders are practicing Christians today.

The Cook Islands have been an independent nation under the protectorate of New Zealand since 1976. Like so much of the South Pacific, there was a marked contrast between the modern and the undeveloped. Much of the modernization came with the building of the international airport in the mid-1970s. Since the large jets have been landing there, goods from the west have become more plentiful and Rarotonga's way of life has changed.

The country's laws used to be quite strict about bringing plants, food and other articles onto the island that could carry agricultural disease. When we landed, the custom's official confiscated my package of pumpkin seeds, purchased in Tahiti, and gave me a receipt so I'd be able get them back when I left. He did allow me to take in a bag of dried apples, a bon-voyage present from a friend in Toronto. I was saving the apples for a rainy day or as security for a famine.

These eastern islands are an ideal vacation spot. They combine the privacy of a tropical paradise with the comfort of western living. The beaches aren't as beautiful as Hawaii or the Seychelles; the nightlife isn't as active as the Caribbean; the Polynesian culture isn't as dominant as in Tonga or Western Samoa; yet there are beautiful beaches, nightly entertainment and a native culture worth exploring. But the main strengths of the islands are their safety, peacefulness and the absence of hassles. There is an atmosphere of contentment. The friendly natives always smile a hello as you walk past.

The main island, Rarotonga, is small enough to drive around in 20 to 30 minutes, making everything accessible. The outer islands are totally remote, and are a hermit's dream.

Tourism is regulated by the government but not in an interfering way. The accommodation is comfortable but not fancy and the food is edible and safe but not gourmet.

Everything is pricey but if you need to you can live on a shoestring budget. There are very few souvenirs or extra places to squander your money.

The climate is pleasantly warm and sunny year round. December to March is the warmest and so it appeals most to travelers from colder hemispheres that want to get away from the ice and snow of winter.

One final advantage: There are no snakes or dangerous animals to avoid.

MESSENGERS FROM HEAVEN

After being picked up at the airport and taken to the Turangi Motel, we were disappointed to find they had no record of our reservation and no place for us to stay. It was New Year's Day and all the other inexpensive hotels were full. I searched my pockets for the name of Daniel's cousin and looked his phone number up in the local phone book.

Sam, his wife Flo, and their two children pulled up in a Toyota truck to rescue us 60 minutes later. Many times on our nine-month journey we were rescued by or met people who were too good to be true. We called these people "Messengers from Heaven". The circumstances and situations were always unexpected, unsolicited, and out of the ordinary. While on holiday, we seem to be much more open to synchronicity. Sam was our first heavenly messenger and he and his family made our stay in Rarotonga exceptional.

Sam was a chubby, smiling Rarotongan who reminded me of a retired linebacker from the Toronto Argonauts football team. He was a former preacher but when we met him he was the speaker of the house of parliament and a well-known and respected man in Rarotonga. He was also one of the leaders of the Bahá'í community and our time in Rarotonga came to have a spiritual focus.

The Bahá'í faith was founded on principles of world peace, love and fellowship. The founder, Bahá'u'lláh, was born in Persia and theorized that all the world's great religions all believed in the same God. Krishna, Buddha, Moses, Jesus and Mohammed, he claimed, were all prophets and leaders. So the Bahá'í faith encompassed and studied all religions. They added Bahá'u'lláh as the modern-day prophet.

The Bahá'í community in the Cook Islands had about 30 members. We were continually being treated to their hospitality and kindness. We were invited for meals, parties, taken on trips up rivers, to beaches, and we were included as part of the community. Proselytizing was not part of their faith although we were exposed each day to their philosophy of love and community. Their faith, hope and idealism were contagious.

SLOWING DOWN

Sam took us to a secluded cabin on the quiet side of the island away from the main town and the tourists. A rocky, shallow, unswimmable beach, 50 yards away provided uncharted territory for Larry to explore. The closest village, where we went for supplies and food, was about a half hour's walk. The best news was that Sam's aunt who owned the cabin charged us only $35 a week. A papaya tree beside our cabin yielded us ready-made breakfasts. All we had to do was climb up on the roof of the cabin to swipe it from the branches.

After the frenzy of leaving Toronto, visiting friends in Los Angeles, and two weeks exploring Tahiti, Rarotonga gave us a chance to slow down. Since there was really nothing to do, few sights to visit, and no telephones to ring, we spent our time reading, writing and strolling.

The most memorable milestone was the transition that took place in our family. From the time Larry was born I had spent a great deal of time with him, and yet as much as I tried to be equal to my wife, Bonnie remained the primary caregiver. Whenever Larry hurt himself or needed some special attention, he would choose Bonnie over me. That changed in Rarotonga. Spending 24 hours a day together for 6 weeks altered the balance and Larry began accepting me as an equal caregiver. If he hurt himself and cried, he'd come to me as readily as his mother.

No more "mommy do". Now we both did.

THE POW-ER

We believed if everyone raised their children in a non-violent atmosphere, then the world would have peaceful, loving children who would grow to become peaceful, loving adults. From the time he was born Larry was not allowed to play with toy guns, or army toys, watch violent shows on television or read violent stories in books. He grew up watching Sesame Street and Mr. Rogers. We preached love, peace and non-violence. The first gun he held and the first movie he ever saw was in Rarotonga.

Bob, a friendly New Zealander who ran a Mr.-Fix-It Store, invited us to be his guest at a Walt Disney movie about a magical cat. Unfortunately, the first movie we had to sit through was a Kung-Fu flick called China Doll. With guns blaring, feet kicking, and hands chopping, everyone was either mauled or killed. The movie was filled with blood and gore and Larry was enthralled.

For three years of his life, we had shielded him from guns, brutality, fighting and killing. Yet after seeing only that one movie all he talked about was guns and killing. He pointed his finger at everyone and went "pow-pow". He picked up every conceivable stick or object and turned it into what he called his "pow-er". One film had destroyed three years of training in non-violence. We were naive enough to believe that if you bring a child up for three years in a peaceful environment you can make a pacifist out of him.

BUG OFF

We moved into our new flat by the beach in a peaceful mood.

We soon discovered the cockroaches had taken over since no one had been living there for some time. We found their droppings in cupboards, drawers, in with the dishes and among the cutlery. At first we imagined we could co-exist with our insect neighbours.

Indeed, people have been sharing living quarters with cockroaches since the dawn of time. Usually cockroaches hide during the day and come out at night. The first night we came home and turned on the light, some 20 or so of the huge critters stopped dead in their tracks. They waited a few seconds and then scurried into hiding. We thought our presence would keep them there. But these were brave souls used to having free reign in the cabin. Soon we began hitting them with our shoe and our trusty broom. But each morning, we continued to find tiny round droppings everywhere.

No more Mr. Nice Guys we decided. We hitchhiked into town and bought a large can of Raid. Armed, we were ruthless. We set out on a campaign to annihilate our insect enemies. In order to be sure we had killed the cockroaches we had to crush them and this made a horrible cracking sound. We developed a technique whereby we screamed loudly as we squished them, which masked the crunch and made their untimely end more tolerable. An important lesson we learned is that cockroaches play dead if you strike them. That's why it was very important to crush them completely. Otherwise they would simply get up and terrorize us again.

Using the Raid we could knock them off the walls and ceiling at a distance and then crush them with our shoes. After a few days of this new offensive the cockroaches retreated. They dared not show their ugly faces around the cabin again, at least in broad daylight.

One memorable battle took place in the middle of the night.

Bonnie got up to go to the washroom. Through a cloud of sleep I could hear shouts and the sound of a broom beating against the walls, bathtub, floor and toilet. There was a skirmish going on between Bonnie and the cockroaches. After about five minutes, the banging stopped and there was silence. I looked over to the washroom and half expected a cockroach to march triumphantly out of the doorway carrying a broom.

Instead I saw Bonnie. Smiling.

SEARCH FOR THE HEALERS

It was through Sam's wife that I began my search for a traditional healer. She suggested that I see the Minister of Health, so I made an appointment to meet with him. A few days later I was sitting across from Dr. Robati in his small spartan office above a post office. The conversation was quite formal and clipped. He explained that the doctors relied on the district health nurses to go into villages and do preventative medicine, like prenatal and well-baby care, immunizations, mosquito eradication and teaching modern hygiene and sanitation. There were public clinics scattered around the Island, and medical care was free to all Cook Islands' inhabitants.

When I asked about traditional healers, he said he really wasn't in contact with them and that I should make an appointment with Dr. Koteka, at the Rarotongan Hospital. The next day I had a tour of the clean, 100-bed hospital and talked to Dr. Koteka, the secretary to the Minister of Health.

Dr. Koteka explained the dramatic changes that were taking place with respect to the health of the Islands' residents. Although there was no cholera, typhoid or malaria, there had been outbreaks of Dengue fever and Ross River fever. Filariasis, ascaris and gastroenteritis were still a concern. Dr. Koteka explained that as the new way of life had changed from a sub-sistence economy, where everyone grew their own food (taro, breadfruit, sweet potato and tropical fruits), to a cash econo-my, where people lived off what they were earning, the nature of disease on the island had changed.

There used to be bartering and sharing and there was always enough food for everyone. But since the start of a cash economy an each-man-for-himself attitude had become more common. In addition, food coming from the west did not have the highest nutritional quality.

"We now are faced with the same sickness as other devel-oping nations. Hypertension, diabetes, cancer, gout and car-diovascular problems were not seen 10 to 20 years ago, but now they have become common," Dr. Koteka said.

It was difficult to reverse the new eating habits. His own children would rather eat white bread, sugar, hot dogs and soda pop than papaya, taro and bananas. Also, along with the attitudinal changes there had been an increase in mental dis-orders, especially anxiety and depression. Dr. Koteka also mentioned the increased incidence of cigarette smoking, alco-hol-related problems and motor-vehicle accidents. We would witness the same negative changes in all the traditional soci-eties we visited.

Although informative, Dr. Koteka did not know any tradi-tional healers; he suggested I visit the public health outpatient department and talk to Dr. Mokotupu, Director of Public Health. Dr. Mokotupu introduced me to three public health nurses. The district health nurses talked to me at great length about what they did and interrogated me for about an hour to ensure I was sincere. They finally decided to let me in on a secret. It seemed that one of the traditional healers was the gardener of the Public Health Clinic. So they took me out to the field behind the clinic to meet Tapua.

Tapua was a short, barefooted, toothless, old man in Bermuda shorts and a yellow, rayon, short-sleeved shirt. He smoked a cigarette and was raking leaves when I first met him. He didn't speak any English but told the nurses I could come back with an interpreter and he would talk with me. We set up a time and place to meet. When I visited him later at his brother's place, I found him to be one of the humblest men I had ever met. He believed that healing came from God and that he was merely a medium for God's work to be done. The healers, or Taungas, were chosen for their qualities of devotion, kindness and humility. The knowledge was passed down from one generation to another.

Tapua worked essentially with massage plus herbal remedies from native plants and trees. He would diagnose an ailment by looking at the person's general appearance but he often relied on pulse diagnosis to tell him what was wrong.

However, he did not use the radial pulse like the healers in China, but placed his thumb a few finger lengths above the under crease of the wrist. He would then attempt to relieve the problem by massaging pressure points not dissimilar to the Japanese acupuncture technique called shiatsu. He would also advise patients to collect certain berries, bark, leaves and roots and mix them together for external or internal use.

Interestingly, Tapua expressed concern about the nuclear testing in French Polynesia. He felt that nuclear radiation affected the air, water supply and the ocean and predicted problems in years to come from this testing.

Tapua, who was 50 at the time, had been healing for 32 years and did not receive any payment for his work. He could be called upon any time, any place to treat people. He often got calls in the middle of the night. If a person were very ill, he would take them to his own house and care for them there. Tapua was a humble, quiet, patient yet powerful man. He lived in almost complete poverty without any material possessions.

When I met with him Tapua placed his thumb a couple of finger lengths above my wrist and pressed down on what he said was my pulse. He told me after feeling my pulse that I had a problem with my eyes and that given enough time he could help me. It was true that I was shortsighted and later regretted not going back to him and giving him a chance.

The natives chose whether to go to the traditional local healers, the Taunga, or to modern medical doctors. Very often the people go to the local healer first and, if not satisfied, would seek more modern medical aid. Some medicine men cured people by summoning spirits in dreams, while others like Tapua used massage in addition to herbal remedies.

In Rarotonga I sought out another traditional healer. This required me to travel to a secluded village. Papa Ma lived in squalor, in a small metal shack with a dirt floor and two big rooms that were home to about 13 people. He was very old, had large swollen legs and walked with a cane. Although Papa Ma and his wife had very little, they shared what they had. They even gave Larry three beautiful handmade shell necklaces.

Papa Ma believed that the herbal remedies he used came from God. The remedies, he said, came often in the form of dreams. He thought I looked like a humble person and he trusted me. He would share his cure for cancer, diabetes and high blood pressure. He said that I would be the first with whom he would share his knowledge, and he felt that it was

132

time for the old and the new to meet. He explained, "We must teach each other what we know, and the time has come when there must be a coming together of the traditional healers and the modern medical doctors."

He told me his secret formula:

Take 12 new sprouting leaves of the breadfruit plant. Pick 12 flowers of the tiare Maori tree: it must be the flower that's going to bloom tomorrow. Take one teaspoon of ground yagona (ground root of the pepper plant). Pound the flowers and leaves together; then add one heaping teaspoon of yagona to the pounded leaves. Wrap the pounded leaves, flowers and powder in a clean cloth, squeeze the juice into boiling water, about one inch in a glass. Add 50 ml. of castor oil to the mixture and stir well. Pray before drinking the mixture and follow it with a warm cup of coffee. Do not have any alcohol for three months after taking the medicine and do not take any other medical drugs during this time. Do not have any cold drinks after drinking the medicine and drink only warm water with no sweetener. After the fifth visit to the toilet, drink cold water to stop the runs.

He told me to come back the next day, so he could make up the remedy for me to take back to my country to give to somebody with cancer. The next day, I hitchhiked by motorcycle to his place, picking up the remedy and carrying it with me throughout my whole journey. By the time I brought it back to Canada it had rotted so I never had a chance to test it out.

Every doctor I spoke with acknowledged the power of the local healers. They told me that often modern medicine could do nothing to help certain cases, yet after seeing the medicine man, they were sometimes cured. Some doctors even sent their patients to the Taunga if they had no solution for an ailment.

133

When it came time to leave Rarotonga, I was saddened. We were met at the airport by Judy, one of the beautiful women from the Bahá'i' community. She waited with us for our departing flight, and gave us fresh-flower leis, as well as other gifts. We felt that we truly belonged to this beautiful island, and that we had met friends whom we would one day meet again.

When we crossed the international dateline, a strange thing happened. We lost a day. Today became tomorrow and we headed on to Fiji.

CHAPTER TWELVE
FIJI – KAVA, CARDS AND FAITH

Cannibalism, fire walking, witchcraft and, almost equally horrific, duty-free shopping are all part of Fiji's fame that lures the tourist to these South Pacific Islands.

For almost 100 years, Fiji was a colony of Great Britain. In 1970 it became a self-governing state, an independent member of the British Commonwealth and has been adjusting to its independence ever since. About half the population of Fiji are Indians from India brought by the British to work the sugar plantations; a little less than half are native Fijians, and Europeans account for less than one percent.

Especially noteworthy is the manner in which the two separate people, Indian and native Fijian, live together. They each have their own customs, language, culture and philosophy. When we were there in 1975 the Indians, by and large, ran the commercial affairs, professions and shops. The native Fijians, a cross of Micronesian, Melanesian and Polynesian races, worked in government, the tourist industry and trades. The two elements of this dual society remained apart socially and culturally. There was little intermarriage.

As in other South Pacific Islands, there is quite a contrast between modern medicine and the traditional healers. There is a further subdivision of Fijian healers and Indian healers. Residents visit both orthodox medical doctors and local healers with equal frequency. The healers are quite varied in their talents, using everything from massage, herbs and prayer, to black magic and playing cards.

Dr. R.M. Rattan, from the ministry of health, told me that the Fijians had "made a grave mistake to focus on modern medical technology and science and totally turn their backs on what the traditional healers had to offer." He feared much of the healing knowledge passed on through generations had already been lost. Apparently since I had been there in 1981 the government was taking more of an interest in traditional Fijian medicine.

Dr. Sally Worthington was trained as a doctor in Australia and came to Suva, the capital of Fiji, in 1975. She worked in general practice and sometimes referred problems to local healers. She related that back problems, arthritic conditions and other musculosketal diseases responded well to the massage and manipulation practised by the traditional healers.

Hookworm, anaemia, and malnutrition were not uncommon. With the changing patterns of people's eating habits, there was a changing pattern of disease similar to that in Rarotonga and other South Pacific countries. The native Fijian once had a diet rich in taro, coconut, tropical fruit and seafood, which was quite high in fibre and always fresh. The Indian would rely on rice, meat or vegetarian dishes high in protein.

As the country became more modernized, both groups started to eat more canned, processed and sugary foods of less nutritional value. Many people blamed the increasing rates of cancer, heart disease, diabetes and hypertension on the changing diet. Rural mothers often had hookworm and iron deficiency and gave birth to many children with severe anaemia.

Also disturbing was the fact that breast-feeding had been steadily declining. As women entered the job market and established careers, the situation got worse. A one-year study of admissions in the major general hospital in Suva discovered that clinical malnutrition was much higher in bottle fed babies than in breast-fed ones. Of the hospital admissions for malnutrition in 1979, 80 percent were bottle-fed, 12 percent were entirely breast-fed, and eight percent were breast-fed with bottle-fed supplements.

KAVA CEREMONY

Wati was a big-boned, heavy-set, Fijian woman in a long blue flowered dress with her name tattooed prominently on her forearm. She had charisma and carried herself in a powerful, yet distant way. I was grateful to share "Yagona" or "kava" with her and three other clients who came to her to be healed.

Yagona is the ground root of the pepper plant, Piper methysticum. It is the ceremonial and the national drink of Fiji; its preparation and consumption are strictly ritualized and solemnly performed.

The five of us sat in silence on the floor in a circle around the kava bowl, a large wooden container where the root is ground into powder and mixed with water. Wati instructed one member of our circle to begin. The hostess Peggy, ceremoniously stirred the muddy-looking water, and in sequence around the circle, kava was poured from one bilo (a half-coconut shell) to another. I clapped my cupped hands once before receiving the bilo, and after swallowing the almost taste-less liquid in one long gulp, I handed the bilo back to Peggy and then clapped three more times. The ritual was performed as each person was handed the kava. After the bilo had gone around the circle once, we began to talk.

The healer said I was the first medical doctor she had ever spoken with. She said she liked my presence and was going to help me in any way possible. Like Tapua from Rarotonga, Wati said it was time for the meeting of modern and old knowledge.

137

She quoted the scriptures saying you cannot plan for the future without looking into the past.

Wati had been healing for 15 years. Ancestral spirits had chosen her, possessed her and put her through a three-year trial period, during which her patience, tolerance and attitude were tested. She said her healing came from God, although she also had many spirits who helped her. She listened to an inner voice that guided her work. People came to her with all kinds of problems from medical to marital to legal. Sometimes she would receive the cure in a dream or she might see an image of the plant necessary for each patient's problem.

After talking for a bit, it was time for another round of kava. Once again the bowl was stirred and kava passed to each person in order. Afterwards, Wati took out a deck of regular playing cards. As she placed the cards in a special pattern, she told one of the women Angela about her past, present and future life. She quickly established a good rapport with her client. Wati told her about her problems with her husband, about her future trip overseas next November, about her menstrual cramps and irregularities, and her competition at work. Wati gave her instructions about leaving five lemon leaves in her pillowcase at night, touching the left side of the doorpost before entering her house that night, and about how it was necessary to counteract a black witch who was cursing her life.

Finally, she uttered a prayer, placed her hands over the young woman's head, turned her around, held Angela's hands and finally, cradled her knees. For another 20-cent piece, she would say a prayer to ward off a burglar who was going to rob her place in the upcoming weeks. I wondered to myself if this was preventive medicine at its best.

This particular young woman seemed quite impressed with

Wati's clairvoyant abilities. I must confess that what Wati told me about my mother, my house in Toronto, and things about my personal health were fuzzy and inaccurate.

After a few more rounds of kava the next client, Barbara, went off with Wati to another room. Medical doctors offered this woman no hope of becoming pregnant. Wati's apparent success rate with infertility was well known, so Barbara was willing to try. Wati used a special oil and hot water and gave her client a massage. She put her fingers into Barbara's vagina and "tipped" her womb into the "proper position."

The Yagona ceremony lasted the afternoon and on into early evening. The immediate after-effect was a tingling tongue and a somewhat numb body. After awhile, I entered a dream-like state and found myself extremely relaxed and enjoying the company of this group. The Yagona had dulled my scientific brain.

As night fell and the last round of kava was poured, I found myself wanting to believe in Wati's healing ability. Whether she was actually a psychotherapist, hypnotist and priest rolled into one, or a powerful healer, I could not say. People trusted her and believed in her power.

Like most people in Fiji, I believe modern medicine and traditional healing can and should — survive side by side. I had just scratched the surface of traditional healing with my visit to Wati, the first spiritual healer I ever met. The heady kava no doubt helped make me more open to her way of healing. Wati, along with Tapua and Papa Ma of Rarotonga, led me to a treasure of knowledge that had been hidden from Western culture.

Our next stop was New Zealand.

CHAPTER THIRTEEN
MAORIS, TAHUNGAS AND A MAGICAL PLANT

The Maori, the native Polynesian people of New Zealand, have their origin in a history that has challenged archaeologists and linguists for centuries. Generally, it is believed the Islands of the Pacific were first settled by people from Asia, although an alternative theory claims a possible American origin for the Polynesian ancestry.

It is difficult to fix the period when the voyages of Pacific Island people to New Zealand began, but legend has it the first Polynesian to visit New Zealand was an explorer called Kupe in about 950 A.D. There were various waves of migration after that, and the names of the canoes and their captains and crews are still remembered by the Maori and are important features of their history and genealogy.

Most Maori live on the North Island of New Zealand. We went to Wellington, the capital city, to learn something about the local healers.

Dr. Sidney Mead, who at the time was professor of anthropology at Victoria University, explained that when the Maori people get sick they go either to their own medicine men, called Tahungas, or to modern medical doctors. For certain problems, they seek modern medical advice, but for others, they know the Tahunga could help them more. The Tahunga approaches most problems from a spiritual point of view and believes that most problems arise on the spiritual level. Therefore the cure includes the spiritual, as well.

As in other Polynesian societies, the Tahunga's knowledge is passed down from one generation to another by word of mouth — usually through families. Our first contact with Maori medicine was during a drive from Helensville to Auckland on the North Island.

The friendly Maori woman who picked us up hitchhiking was taught all about herbs by her grandmother. She pointed out various plants growing by the road that were used for certain problems. During the one-hour drive we saw remedies for eczema, tummy aches, haemorrhoids and warts. Many Maoris have quite a good knowledge of the use of herbs as medicine.

We talked to Joseph, one Tahunga who told us about his training. When he was a teenager he was extremely interested in healing and began to spend hours with his uncle, who was the Tahunga of the area. His formal training took place over many years. If he was to have a special session with his uncle, he might fast for two days before. Then, around midnight, he would join his uncle by an open fire. This would be the setting for the knowledge and art of healing to be passed on.

First, Joseph was taught genealogy. Very often, around the fire he would go into a trance, and his uncle would teach him about the family history of all the families in the village. In our medical schools, we learn to take a family history by asking about diabetes, allergies, cancer, epilepsy, and other common illnesses, usually going back to the grandparents of the patient.

The Tahunga's knowledge, in contrast, goes back to the beginning of Maori history. In this hypnotic state, each family is traced back to the original canoes that landed in New Zealand. So the Tahunga would not only know the detailed social history of each individual in the village, he also learned about each person's medical history.

For example, if two generations before a relative had epilepsy, this would be remembered. If a curse were placed on a family because of some wrongdoing generations ago, this would be known by the Tahunga and taken into consideration when diagnosing and treating a patient. If doctors today had such an extensive historical picture at their fingertips, it would certainly give them a greater perspective on their patients. Even before dealing with the specific problem at hand, they would have a head start in understanding what this person was all about.

Next Joseph learned about herbs and plants and how they could be used to treat certain ailments. The remedies involved local bark, leaves, berries and roots of the various plants and trees in the area.

One Tahunga whom we visited was quite famous for his cancer cure. We heard many anecdotal stories about bladder and prostate cancers being completely cured by his herbal drinks. A generous and hospitable European New Zealander, named Tony, who had picked us up hitchhiking and actually invited us to stay at his home, took us to meet this Tahunga. One of his friends was dying of end-stage bladder cancer and the medical doctors had apparently given up on him.

Tony told us that the Tahunga had cured his friend of the cancer by getting him to drink a special formula made from a local plant. Tony took us to the centre of downtown Helensville, next to the men's public lavatory and showed us a huge aloe vera plant that the Tahunga used in healing. Each week, this New Zealander would pick a certain quantity of the fleshy leaves of the plant. He would take it to the Tahunga who would mix it with water and a secret formula. After three months of drinking only this remedy, he was apparently free of any trace of cancer. I was told that years later, he was still in perfect health.

During his training, the Tahunga also learned all the prayers and incantations for various situations. Since the Maori were so connected to the spiritual side of life, there was a chant or prayer uttered to heal the spirit of sick people. It was even common practice, and accepted by most hospitals, for the elders to visit, say their prayers and incantations right in the sick person's hospital room.

It was customary for some Tahungas to ceremoniously wash their hands before and after seeing patients. Although this may be hygienically sound, in fact, the practice allowed the healer to cleanse himself spiritually before seeing the patient, and afterward washing himself of the burden he had just shared. Along with the hand washing, a prayer could also be recited.

Before major healing events, the Tahunga might fast for a couple of days to cleanse himself completely, and prepare himself before helping with a major problem. We were told that if there was an exceptionally difficult problem and the Tahunga felt it was too much to handle alone, he might call together many people of the village to share the burden of healing.

In Western society there seems to be an increasing incidence of suicide, divorce and drug addiction among physicians. We are rarely taught in medical school how to handle the many demands being placed on us as healers. Some experts believe doctors experience burnout after being in practice for many years because we don't know how to take care of ourselves.

The Tahungas were always conscious of the fact that being a helper puts a certain stress on one's life, and they were taught how to handle this through prayer, cleansing and communal support.

Many Tahungas claimed to possess extrasensory perception.

They believed they have the ability to predict the future, see visions of past happenings and have insights into people's consciousness. Many received wisdom and important messages in dreams. It seemed that they did not let this intuitive side of their brain fall into disuse.

FAMILY SUPPORT

One of the basics of Maori life was the communal attitude of the people. They emphasized sharing and banded together in times of need. One custom was the calling together of a whole village for days at a time to focus on one person's problem. In this way, the extended family could offer their support.

In North America the extended family is no longer such a dominant force, and the nuclear family is falling apart. The concept of calling together every member of a person's entire extended family can be a powerful tool. In the Maori tradition, this practice is an extremely successful way of helping individuals and families work out their difficulties.

The native healing practices were still alive and seemed to complement the science, technology and modern medicine of New Zealand. The focus on genealogy, family support, prayer and trance, and the Maori's knowledge of the local flora and fauna impressed me. The practices of the traditional healers of the South Pacific would later be mimicked by healers that I would meet in Asia, Africa and even North America.

CHAPTER FOURTEEN
ALMOST EATEN ON SAFARI

The majority of people who live in big cities are completely cut off from contact with animals except for cats, dogs, robins, squirrels and cockroaches. Children growing up in a city often learn about animals first through books, television and movies. They develop their own excitement and infatuation with animals of the jungle and give these exotic creatures personalities and human traits. They build friendships with characters like Yogi Bear, Donald Duck, Kermit the Frog and Barney.

When the fantasy of knowing these characters turns to the reality of seeing these animals in the zoo, I have noticed there at times can be a tremendous disappointment. I sometimes feel sad when I go to the zoo or circus because I have seen many situations where the standard of care is quite poor. It is tragic to see beautiful animals so badly abused and restricted.

I thought it would be important to see the animals in the wild before they are destroyed. Since I have always dreamed of going to Africa to see the wild animals, you can imagine my excitement when Bonnie and I took Larry, then three, to Kenya to go on safari to the Masai Mara Game Reserve.

We flew from the Seychelles, one of the most beautiful islands in the world, to Nairobi the capital of Kenya. All of the safaris were very expensive so we joined up with a camping company called Kimbla Travel, which took us on a four-day camping trip through the game reserve at the height of the season for the migratory wildebeests. I just could not wait for my son to see all the animals and for us to see the jungle through his eyes.

A month earlier, in Sri Lanka, we had seen the cartoon movie, "The Jungle Book". Larry identified strongly with Mowgli, the jungle boy who was raised by a pack of wolves and befriended by some delightful animal characters. We tried to get him excited about the safari too by talking about how great it was going to be.

When we finally got into our safari wagons and began to spy lions, zebras, giraffes and elephants running free across the plains, Bonnie and I were jumping with joy, snapping photos, pointing fingers and screaming with glee. However, as soon as the vehicle started moving, Larry closed his eyes and went soundly to sleep. He didn't wake up until we got back to our campsite. At three he just couldn't seem to relate to the real thing and the task of spotting animals was difficult for him. He didn't remember a thing about our day excursions into the reserve.

On the last night of our safari, we were camped by a tiny stream. All along we had been assured that our campsite was safe and there were supposed to be guards around the campfire guarding us with rifles. At about one o'clock in the morning we heard something eating at the side of our tent. At first we were afraid to peek out and see what was there but Bonnie had to get up to pee and bravely looked out to find huge water buffaloes grazing around the tents. They seemed to be docile and minding their own business so she relieved herself beside our tent. The guards were still sitting up-asleep.

When she came back we cuddled into our warm sleeping bag and listened to our small son breathing peacefully beside us. All of a sudden we heard thunderous hoof beats galloping by our tent. We sat up frozen with fear. Then came the most horrible high-pitched shrieking and gasping noises from across the stream. It sounded to us like a donkey groaning. We huddled closer to each other and after awhile we fell asleep.

We woke up early the next morning with the sunrise and decided to find out what had happened. To our surprise there were large paw tracts right through our campsite going across the river. Curiously we followed the tracts and some 50 yards away we found a large intact zebra skin, all bloodied, and completely cleaned of flesh right down to the skin. We saw vultures up in the trees and flying overhead with big bloody bones hanging from their jaws.

Two lions had chased a herd of zebra right through our campsite. One zebra didn't make it. All of a sudden we were thankful that this was our last night in the wild and it was time to get back to Nairobi. We felt lucky that the lions preferred zebra meat to tourist meat.

CHAPTER FIFTEEN
INDONESIA-LETS GO ARCHIPELAGO

MAGICAL BALI

The Republic of Indonesia is made up of a series of islands sprinkled across the Indian Ocean. It is one of the world's largest archipelagos, and one of the largest Moslem countries. We have been fortunate enough to visit the islands of Indonesia many times — Java, Sulawesi, Sumatra, Irian Jaya — but of all the places in the world, the island of Bali is our favourite and keeps drawing us back.

It is a small island only 140 km by 80 km that lies just south of the equator. The majority of the three million inhabitants are Hindu and it is the only predominantly Hindu island in Indonesia.

Bali has been a magical place for us. Green terraced rice fields, volcanic mountains, coconut forests, endless beaches, and exotic flowers are only a part of the island's spectacular natural beauty. The quality of the paintings, woodcarvings and jewellery make me want to reach into my pockets and buy everything.

But the amazing artistic life and the natural beauty are over-shadowed by the spiritual consciousness of the people. Celebration is part of daily life. Blessing and prayers go hand in hand with births, deaths, vacations, even well digging. Every event is a spiritual event. Over the years we've taken part in temple festivals, cremations, weddings, tooth-filing cere-monies, building blessings and full-moon celebrations.

YOU CAN'T GO BACK

Very often vacations can be a way of tracking how you've changed and grown over the years. It's a marker that helps you to take stock of your life. Many travelers believe you can't go back to a place you've been because it won't be the same. You can never step into the same river twice.

When we visited Bali in 1975, Bonnie and I felt that this was our paradise. We had a community of friends and there was a warm, open spirit about Kuta Beach that was unique. People would smile as you passed by, everyone would say hello and there was a feeling of camaraderie among the travelers. The Balinese were genuinely friendly and almost innocent in their interactions with tourists. They were also spiritual people who appreciated life and did not focus on materialism.

Of course, Bali was tremendously romantic for us then because we had no children and this was like our second honeymoon. The weather was beautiful, the beaches were idyllic, the food was inexpensive and remarkably tasty and Bali had a spiritual way of life that we had searched for in various countries.

Before going to Bali we traveled through Australia. When we visited the emergency room of one of the hospitals to get a gamma globulin shot to protect us from hepatitis, coincidently the nurse who gave us the shot had just come back from Bali. She told us a little about Bali and recommended we stay at a small hotel in Kuta Beach called Losmen Sareg.

In those days Kuta Beach's airport was fairly primitive. When we exited the terminal there were hordes of guides crowding around us, all wanting to take us to their hotels. Out of all the men who were shouting at us to come to their hotel, we chose a smiling, polite, relatively quiet man to whom we were somehow attracted. Synchronisticly, this man whose name was Alit, turned out to be from Losmen Sareg.

Losmen Sareg was a small pension hotel run by an elderly jeweller and his family. All members of the family took part in the upkeep and the care of the place. We felt at home with this family and got to know them as well as anyone could after three weeks. We lived in a fairly Spartan room that had two beds with white sheets, our own seatless toilet and a hose on the wall that served as our cold shower. Tea was left in a container on the porch and we were welcome to as much tea and bananas as we wanted.

Across from our room was the family residence where we could see the manager's young wife, bare-breasted, preparing meals, cleaning house and feeding her child. Like part of the family, we were included in their ceremonies and they helped us with all our problems and requests.

We also fell into a community of friends — some Americans, Floriano the Italian artist, a couple of Aussies and a few British travelers. They became our second family. It felt like "Woodstock" was alive and well in Kuta Beach. Free exchanges of traveling tips and a mellowness of spirit permeated everyone.

Just as the Hindu artists, musicians, mystics, dancers and intelligentsia from Indonesia fled to Bali during the Moslem invasion in the 14th century, the last of the Hippie generation with ideals of peace, love and brotherhood dancing in their heads seemed to flock here in the early '70s.

The streets were so quiet you could hear the whisper of bicycles passing on the main road to the beach. From Bemo

151

Corner, the first crossroad up from the beach, the narrow paved road was dotted with a few small hotels, restaurants and stands selling clothes and trinkets. A few more pensions and restaurants were scattered along the roads at right angles to the beach and down unpaved paths. But the town was small. Indeed, you could learn where all its restaurants, banks, shops and hotels were in just a few days.

The sunsets were spectacular. Everyone would meet on the beach around 5:00 p.m. and watch the sun fall into the ocean, lighting the sky in reds, yellows, oranges, and blues. I was amazed that nature could create so many different shades and tints and hues. If I had seen a painting with the colors in these sunsets I would have thought it was just the artist's imagination. But after watching the evening escapade on Sunset Beach, I realized no artist could ever capture these colors on canvas.

After the sunset show we would wander off for a supper of freshly prepared rice, noodles, shish kebob, and fish. We could stuff ourselves for anywhere from three to six dollars — for the two of us. Fruit stands were set up on corners and the Balinese would squeeze and crush mangosteens, salaks, papaya, bananas, and mangoes in a hand juicer, mix in ice and sell it for about 20 cents a glass. The taste was worth the risk of a Bali-belly. Thankfully, we always remained healthy.

In 1975 the pace in Kuta was leisurely, the people were gentle and everything was a celebration or ceremony.

EVERYTHING HAD CHANGED

Six years later, Kuta was no longer recognizable. When we returned in 1981, with our three-year-old son, we mourned the loss of our innocence. We had changed and so had Bali. Javanese and foreign business people had snapped up property and opened huge hotels, restaurants and fancy shops with solid walls, replacing the open stalls plastered with straw mats. On our previous visit there were but a few scattered buildings, now there was a solid wall of them lining the roads through the village.

The once secluded beach was filled with hawkers continually haranguing tourists to buy carvings, clothes and cold drinks. The Australian Pub culture was creeping into town and the streets were noisy with hundreds of motorcycles with Balinese teenagers in blue jeans chirping "Hello mate", in a heavy Australian accent. In 1975 there were few cars; everyone traveled by bicycle. By 1981 there were so many vehicles it was actually dangerous to walk the streets and the air and noise pollution were intolerable.

Because we now had Larry, we were concerned that Losmen Sareg would no longer be suitable for our stay. It did not have overhead fans in the rooms and we were worried that with the intense heat we would need some form of air conditioning. For Larry's comfort, we wanted to upgrade our accommodations slightly. So we sought out a fancier place closer to the beach that offered us the luxury of an overhead fan. At the Kodja Beach Hotel our room was almost twice as big and was in a much more elegant location.

After a few days, we decided to visit Losmen Sareg and speak to the family we had met there. We had written to them a few times but did not let them know that we were returning to Bali. When we walked into the compound and embraced Sareg and his family I was struck by the fact that they did not seem to have changed in the six years since we had been there. Even the compound and lodging looked the same except for a few trees reaching closer to the clouds. Although his children had grown up and his grandchild was now a little boy, Sareg and his family were still the same smiling, friendly, people we had left in 1975.

We tried to explain why we weren't staying at their Losmen this time. I wanted to be honest and said we needed a fan in the room and that we were concerned about Larry and wanted a better accommodation. But they could not understand why we didn't want to come back to their hotel. The whole scene saddened me and suddenly I began to cry. When they saw the tears streaming down my face, they didn't know what to do. They didn't understand that I was crying for the loss of our innocence, and the way things used to be.

I was no longer carefree; I had responsibilities. I had a son, a house, a car, and a medical practice. It was as if I were abandoning their friendship for my own comfort and convenience. They were still the simple, easy-going, friendly people that I remembered but it was not the same Bali. Our friends were no longer there, the people had become more materialistic and the invasion of tourists and Indonesians from other islands had dramatically changed not only the way that Kuta Beach looked but the way it operated. The lost dream would never return. We were no longer footloose and fancy free. We learned you can't go back. So we mourned the old way for a few days and then began to enjoy ourselves in a new and different way. We still loved the place so much that we stayed a whole marvellous month. We made new friends, found new favourite restaurants, and watched Larry frolicking in the waves for hours.

And the sunsets hadn't changed a single, solitary hue. The best things in life were still free.

BALIAN USADA, URUT AND KETAKSON

When ill, many Balinese would seek out a Balian, or traditional healer. There were certain medical problems for which they sought a medical doctor's care, such as infections. However, there were other conditions for which the Balinese turned to traditional healers. In addition, it was less expensive and more convenient to go to a Balian.

There were three main types of healers. The first, called a Balian Usada, used herbal remedies that were often written in ancient books, or Lontar. These books contained recipes for a wide array of medical problems and were passed down from one generation to another.

The second type of healer, called appropriately bonesetters or Balian Urut specialized in problems of the musculoskeletal system. These healers massaged and manipulated patients with arthritis, sprains, pains and related complaints.

Then there were the spiritual healers who believed that people got sick on a spiritual level and that their physical bodies were then affected. One type of spiritual healer was called a Ketakson, who went into a meditative state and received messages about people and their cure.

The first healer I visited in Bali was a 73-year-old Balian named Pekak Mangku. He was a chubby, toothless, old man whose face and body were covered in black moles. He wore a black-checkered sarong and sat on a bed covered with a woven straw mat. To one side was a small prayer altar, burning incense.

His first patient came to him with a sore wrist. Apparently four days earlier, the man had fallen on his outstretched arm and since then his wrist had been sore whenever he moved it. Few words were spoken. First the healer touched the wrist and while exploring all parts of the wrist, he massaged different points on the hand and forearm.

These points, surprisingly enough, corresponded to the acupuncture pressure points used in Chinese acupuncture. After working on the wrist he went up the forearm to the elbow and finally massaged points throughout the upper arm. After a few moments the man could move his wrist without any pain.

But the treatment did not stop there. The man removed his shirt and the healer massaged his neck and shoulders. Then the healer gently manipulated and cracked the man's neck and shoulders, much like a chiropractor. He believed the man's problem was not focused just in the wrist but affected the neck, back, shoulders and upper arm.

Pekak Mangku took three years of formal training from various healers in Bali when he was young. After that he learned his craft through experience. He confided in me that after 50 years of healing, he felt he still did not know enough and was continually learning.

After he massaged and manipulated the stiff neck of the Balinese medical doctor who brought me to this man in the first place, he took me to his one inpatient. In another part of his home lay a 10-year-old-boy who had been in a motor vehicle accident two weeks previously in a town called Singaraja. The boy had suffered a fractured femur and had been brought for treatment by his family.

The boy's left leg was in makeshift traction, tied to the end of a bed by a stretchy piece of long cloth. A piece of cloth soaked in a kind of plaster was tied around his thigh; bound around the cloth were bamboo sticks about four inches in length that circled his thigh. The plan was to keep the boy like this for about a month and then he would be able to walk. His parents chose Pekak Mangku over the local hospital and sent his older sister along to look after him.

This was the first time I had ever witnessed traditional healing where I questioned whether it was the best possible treatment available. Both the Balinese medical doctor and I felt that the traction was insufficient. This young boy's femur would not heal properly and he might well have a permanent limp.

SPIRITUAL HEALER

A few days later I traveled down a dirt road in search of a famous spiritual healer named Wayan. A line up of cars and motorcycles snaked along the outside of his brick-walled compound. Wayan was a busy man. Apparently he saw more than 100 people a day. He blessed babies, consulted on personal problems, and even saw people in groups. In this kind of group therapy Wayan took people with similar problems and brought them together. He sat behind an altar lined with flowers, a single naked light bulb hanging over his head, and preached to the people.

My medical doctor translator said that his patients fell into three groups: those who were sick because another person had cast a curse on them; those whose food was being poisoned by someone else; and those who apparently became ill because someone hid metal objects in their rooms and drained their strength.

The Balian removed curses, told people to go back and

search their rooms for nails, knives, and other metal objects, and warned them about the food they were eating. People came from all over Bali to hear his advice and benefit from his wisdom. Some even came from other Indonesian islands.

How did this spiritual healer get started? Simply. He was walking down the road in a northern part of Bali about four years earlier, when suddenly a "vision" came to him. In this vision he was told to go to Sukawati and there he would help people. He was told what house to visit and he stayed there three days praying. Soon people began to come to him for help. I thought to myself that this would be a unique way for a medical doctor to open up a new practice.

With my translator's help, I told Wayan that I wanted to learn more about spiritual healing. He invited me to spend three nights with him at his home and he would teach me what I needed to know. I explained that it would be difficult to leave my wife and three-year-old son. Besides I could not speak Balinese.

He mulled over my predicament and finally said that if I went home and slept in my hotel room, for the next three nights spiritual healing would be taught to me in English in my dreams. Alas, three nights passed and nothing came to me in my sleep but a few mosquitoes. When I awoke, I was not enlightened.

I was simply groggy.

SHRINK RAPPED

I spoke to Dr. Denny Thong a psychiatrist who, at the time, was the director of the psychiatric hospital in Bali. The Balinese people, he said, are peaceful, contented, and non-aggressive. They seldom showed hostility and most people suppressed their emotions. The only open aggressiveness shown was on the roads. In traffic, everyone competed ruthlessly for space and power. It's a frightening experience to drive in Bali. Not surprisingly traffic accidents are one of the country's major causes of death and disability.

Dr. Thong believed the people take out their aggressive feelings through dance and other art forms. They also used trance as a catharsis. For example, many dances performed regularly in the community tell simple stories of good versus evil. The people watching identify with both sides and often go into a trance along with the players. It is all right for people to express anger, shriek and fight with masks and costumes on. This is an acceptable and valuable outlet for suppressed feelings.

The Balian serve as healers for the people, Denny said. They are a stabilizing influence on the community, acting in a sense like a community psychiatrist. Many spiritual healers used trances, magic and voices to convince people what path they should follow. Speaking from a trance absolved them of any responsibility for what they advised so they could make judgments and suggestions that they might not ordinarily say. Also, because they went into trance or used magic, their advice was so dramatically given that people tended to pay more attention and heed the advice.

Take the example of a man who comes to a Balian with a headache. Most headaches are not brain tumors or serious infections but are caused by stress or other psychological causes. The spiritual healer might go into a trance and take the patient along with him. Then he might, using a magic slight of hand, pull out a nail from the patient's head, pronouncing this the cause of the pain. The nail would be visible proof that something had been wrong and to Balinese patients this magic seemed to cure the problem. It was certainly more effective than telling them their problem was psychological.

Dr. Thong believed that healers still had a great power over people and that a lot could be learned from them. He and his colleagues were trying to work with Balians to educate them about hygiene and preventive medicine practices. He wanted medical doctors to study how the healers practiced so that their tools could be used by to advance the common good. He especially saw the trance state as a powerful healing tool and believed it was important to study and understand how we might use it in modern medicine.

The Balian also speaks the language of the people and structures his treatment in ways that the average person understands. All too often in my travels I felt that the medical profession was not being clearly heard or understood because their spoken language and their body language were alienating them from their patients. Many Balian had a talent for intuitively assessing a person's nature and their problems.

Perhaps doctors start suppressing this part of their brain in medical school and become so scientifically oriented over time that we lose our intuitive sense.

At least that's what a little voice inside keeps telling me.

BALI SPIRIT

It is thought that Hinduism came to Indonesia via India and from there spread to Bali by nomadic mystics and teachers. Hinduism then blended with existing beliefs; the spirits of animals, inanimate objects, human ancestors, and good and evil were worshipped.

Many Balinese believe there is a supreme god called Sang Hyang Widhi Wasa who has many manifestations. The three principle ones are Brahma, the creator; Shiva, the destroyer; and Vishnu, the protector.

Bali is unique in the way prayer, worship and celebration are part of every aspect of daily life. Hindus are supposed to pray three times a day: sunrise, high noon and sunset. Ostensibly most people just pray in the morning.

The woman of the household prepares the food for the day and afterward small offerings of rice, flowers and incense are placed throughout the home — and elsewhere — to bless the spirits who take care of people during their day. An offering might be placed, for example, on the dashboard of a car, on the steps of a house, in the temple that is part of every home, and in the surrounding streets, business shops and tourists' doorways to bless and make life safe.

The number of temples in Bali is truly remarkable. To start with every home has its own temple. This is the most important temple; it preserves the Balinese way of life. Because the temple is part of the home, it makes religion and worship more personal and integral to family life. In the past, family homes in Bali could not be sold, but were passed on from generation to generation. Every family's ancestral spirits, it is believed, inhabit the family temple. Since these spirits watch over the day-to-day life and protect and guide the family, it is extremely important to care for, honor and maintain the family temple.

Every village also has at least three temples. The "Pura Dalem" or temple of the dead is located near the graveyard or cremation area. This is the place for Durga, Shiva's wife. The "Pura Desa" is the temple for the spirits who take care of the village community. This is the domain of Brahma. The "Pura Puseh," or temple of origin, is for the ancestors and lords of the soul. It is dedicated to the village founders and is where Vishnu resides.

Eight temples are considered so important that they are said to be temples for the whole island and they are located in important strategic locations or power points surrounding Bali. Besakih temple, the "mother temple", is located in the centre of Gunung Agung, the largest mountain in the country. The seven other temples radiate the island like spokes of a wheel to protect all sides of the island from bad influences.

In addition to these three types of temples, there are clan temples for groups of families with similar descendants and temples for different organizations like the rice growers co-operative and fishing societies. These are dedicated to the spirits who protect these industries. Then there are shrines or thrones, which aren't really temples, in rice fields, at crossroads and bends in the roads, beside special trees and anywhere there may be spirits lurking. That, by the way, is everywhere.

Not only do the religious pray three times a day in Bali, but they visit the temple every five days, every 15 days, every full moon, every dark moon, and particularly every 210 days on the anniversary of the founding of each temple. The Balinese have a six month calendar so everything is celebrated twice a year. There are also many other holidays and special days when visits to the temple are important.

Ceremonies celebrating the cycle of life are held in the family temple. The birth of a baby, marriage of a young couple and illness of a relative, will all draw the family to the temple to pray. Often family members from all over Bali and Indonesia will return to their homes to pray together during special ceremonies. The focus on ritual and ceremony in daily life ensures that families remain strong and close knit. Even though many young people have been influenced by the worst of Western culture, there is still a strong respect for tradition and custom.

Not a day would go by in Bali that I didn't see women dressed in temple dress with huge baskets laden with fruits, flowers, and food, balanced on their heads, marching single file to a celebration. The celebrations whether they were store openings or temple anniversaries were filled with music, prayer and gifts for the gods. If we were lucky there was also a show of traditional dance and enactment of a centuries-old play.

A TEMPLE FESTIVAL

Once while staying in Candidasa, a small beach resort in eastern Bali, Larry was invited to a temple festival by Made, one of the young men who cleaned the rooms at our hotel. His family temple was celebrating a 210-day anniversary of its founding. I was cautious about letting him go out by himself at age 11, especially by motorcycle at night, so I asked if I could come along.

A motorcycle driver picked us up around 5 p.m. and took us to Tanahampo, a village about five kilometers from our hotel. There, in Made's home, we were treated to biscuits, tea in a glass (as is customary) and introduced to his family. We were dressed in sarongs, a piece of cloth two and a half metres long wrapped around the waist. A rectangular piece of cloth, or sash, is worn on top.

When visiting any temple, everyone must wear a sarong and sash and obey temple custom. Anyone who has an open wound or is menstruating, cannot enter the temple. People who have recently lost a relative cannot enter until three days after the cremation.

Larry and I were warmly included in the temple ceremony,

which took place with us all sitting cross-legged on straw mats on the ground. The priests, dressed in white, sprinkled holy water, distributed flowers, chanted and rang their hand-held temple bells to announce a time for prayer. Much of the prayer was said silently and was intended to be a personal prayer.

In the middle of praying, Made turned to me and asked if there was a problem for me praying in this Hindu ceremony. I replied, "Sin Ken Ken", which means "No problem."

He replied," Of course there is no problem, because there is only one God who is all the same all over the world. Only the form and structure of prayer is different." I agreed.

The ceremony was light, easy-going, and seemed almost festive. We were later introduced to grandfather, uncles, and cousins, and were reminded that Made was related in some way to the hundred or so people in this family temple.

When the prayers and blessings ended, the women picked up their huge baskets of fruit, food, and flowers, balanced them on top of their heads again and paraded home. After being served rice, peanuts, coconut, tuna, coconut milk mixed with meat, and bananas, we were returned to our hotel by the same motorcycle driver.

We had been touched by the welcoming openness of Balinese culture.

SARASWATI

In addition to temple festivals, or Odalans, there are special celebrations called Tumpeks. On these special days inanimate, secular objects are honoured. For example, on certain days offerings are made to weapons such as swords, daggers and spears. Other Tumpeks honour trees, musical instruments, masks, puppets, jewellery and objects made of gold, silver and precious stones.

I was fortunate to be in Bali on a day devoted to Saraswati, the goddess of knowledge. Special prayers were recited with regard to learning, education and books. On this day people are not supposed to read or write. Students gather at temples to ask Saraswati for success in their studies and special ceremonies are held at schools and libraries. Everyone offers thanks for the books they own and for the privilege of learning.

I met Ketut Liyer in Pengosekan, a village outside the city of Ubud, one of the main centres for art. Ketut is a Balian Usada, a healer who relies on healing texts called lontar. These lontar are manuscripts etched on elaborately carved palm leaves in Sanskrit or Kawi and contain the religious knowledge that has been handed down from one generation to another. There are specific lontar that are concerned with healing and these are considered sacred possessions for they contain the wisdom of ancestors.

Ketut's grandfather was a famous healer and teacher of lontar. He prophesied that Ketut would also be a healer. But Ketut had always wanted to be an artist, so he started off down that path. But while he was still young, he became quite ill. He went to a Balian Ketakson, a Balinese healer who goes into an altered state or trance to receive messages from spirits. As I mentioned previously this kind of Balian have the power to foretell the future and discover what is wrong with people who are ill. The Balian told Ketut that he was ill because he was not following his real calling, which was to be a Balian.

Ketut carried himself off home and began reading his great grandfather's lontar. He began healing himself and soon others

165

came to him for help. He continued to read lontar daily and administered the leaves, flowers, roots, and bark of medicinal plants to people who were sick. The lontar helped him to diagnose and treat illness and provided mantras and incantations, to ward off evil spirits and assist with spiritual problems. People came from all over Bali to receive Ketut's advice.

On Saraswati I visited Ketut. Before entering his home, Bonnie and I put on the appropriate sarongs and sashes so we could visit his home temple. Ketut was dressed all in white, with a white scarf around his head. His wide smile, bulged with teeth as he welcomed us into the area of the compound of his house that contained the temple. All the books of the household, as well as his collection of lontar, were piled high in the centre on the wooden altar. Everywhere there were offerings of flowers, fruit and palm leaf decorations. Incense sticks were sticking out of every nook and cranny filling the air with a sweet fragrance.

Throughout the day members of the community and all his patients came to his temple, bringing gifts and offerings and placed them on the platform next to the books. Ketut rang his temple bell and chanted prayers while ceremonial gamelan music played on his tape recorder in the background.

People were squatting on their knees facing the altar in lines as Ketut came around and sprinkled holy water on their heads, all the while chanting a prayer. Holy water was also poured into people's palms. They drank this water while saying prayers silently to themselves.

There was a steady stream of people all afternoon and a festive atmosphere in his home. Meanwhile similar ceremonies were taking place all across the Island. By setting aside a special day twice a year to honour books and learning, the Balinese show their respect and esteem for knowledge and literature. Aspects of life that are often taken for granted thereby become special and are given reverence. The Balinese take the mundane and elevate it to a celebration, giving thanks for every aspect of their life.

BALINESE CREMATION

In 1989 we were living in Ubud, a small town known for its incredible painters. A fellow traveler, Karen, mentioned she was going to a cremation and we asked if we could tag along. So Bonnie, our three children, Karen, our host Agus, his wife and child and I jammed ourselves into a small car around 11 a.m. and traveled seven kilometres along a narrow road to the tiny village of Deng where the cremation took place.

In 1975, during our first visit, Bonnie and I had attended a simple cremation in Ubud where there were only a few tourist faces in the crowd. It was disheartening to return six years later to find that there were cremation tours, organized by professional companies, taking busloads of camera-laden tourists in short shorts to cremations. These companies were charging exorbitant prices to go to a private funeral.

I have always been amazed at the openness of the Balinese people. Many countries throughout the world distrust foreigners or anyone who looks different. But the Balinese welcome foreigners, even at the time of their ceremony for the dead. Can you imagine yourself at the cemetery burying one of your close relatives when a busload of tourists in thongs, singlets, sunhats, sunglasses and video cameras come marching up to the grave site and begins taking photos, talking and laughing, oblivious to the solemness of the event? This was exactly how it felt in 1981 when cremation tours were popping up everywhere.

On this day, however, we were extremely fortunate. We were almost the only foreigners at the cremation, which celebrates the life of the deceased rather than mourning their passing. At cremations the Balinese are solemn but not unhappy.

The Hindus believe that humans are composed of two parts — the body and the soul. When the body dies and is burned, the spirit is released to be reincarnated in paradise, or heaven. Those with good karma or who have performed the right deeds and actions will be released from the cycle of birth and death to join the cosmos and be part of god.

If your karma is good but not perfect, your spirit will return to earth to be reborn in another human being and you will have another opportunity to work on unfinished business. If your actions in life have not been good, you might be reincarnated as an animal.

Most of the time, the cremation is seen as a release of the soul to a higher spiritual plane and freedom from the world of pain and suffering in which we all live, so the Balinese do not mourn. The man who was being cremated at this ceremony was in his 60s and had been sick for 17 years. He had been married but childless. His wife was the only person who looked sad, and even she didn't shed a tear. In Balinese society tears are not acceptable, even from young children. It is considered especially bad for the spirit if tears fall on the body during the ceremony.

It is customary for family members to return home to see the dying person before they pass away. Close relatives will fly in from all over to bid a final farewell and be there when death occurs. The hundred or so participants at this cremation came to the home of the deceased laden with offerings and the day was spent gathered around the family temple.

Balinese homes are actually compounds surrounded by a wall. Inside the wall there is always a garden and separate buildings for each household activity. There would be, for example, one building for cooking, one for washing, another for personal hygiene and another for sleeping. Traditionally most of the buildings have no walls, but are open on all sides and covered with a roof. The family temple can be found in one corner of the compound, usually facing the mother temple on Mt. Agung. Most of these compounds are home to the entire extended family.

When we arrived, the women were sitting in the bedroom, an elevated area made of concrete. Here the body lay resting behind a curtain. They were busy folding palm leaves to make small trays and decorations for the offerings for the cremation ceremony. Other women were in the temple itself arranging food on trays, lighting incense and preparing for the meal and ceremonies that were to follow.

The men were dressed in sarongs, with a sash tied on top. Most also wore a headband. They sat cross-legged around the porch. Tea and cigarettes were passed around as everyone chatted. Some of the men were busy chopping wood, digging holes for posts, building bamboo platforms, roasting pigs, sacrificing chickens and helping prepare the funeral pyre.

Behind the kitchen about 20 men, each with a black and white checkered cloth around his waist and a white headband, sat cross-legged in front of gamelans. These are musical instruments from Indonesia, similar to a xylophone. Throughout the entire day they played these, as well as gongs, drums, and flutes. Their music gave the ceremony a festive spirit.

Around one o'clock, we were called to a buffet lunch. Plates of satay (shishkebab), rice, lentils, cooked vegetables and other special Balinese dishes were set on the table behind the kitchen. The women served themselves first, then the men. After taking food everyone then took seats on the floor to eat their food.

The Balinese do not use forks and spoons. Our son Marc, who was three years old at the time, had great fun smearing rice over his face and clothes. We had taught him so well how to eat with a fork and spoon that he did not know how to eat with his hands. After twenty minutes of practice, however, he too was adept at shoving rice in his mouth.

PREPARING FOR THE AFTERLIFE

At about three o'clock the body was brought from behind the curtain and placed on a homemade bamboo platform. The family gathered around gently touching their kinsman, who lay uncovered on the platform. Older men chanted a lament, while priests' assistants washed his face and head, combed his hair, clipped his nails, and laid flowers around him.

It was a moving moment. Everyone's attention was on the dead person and they were so gentle and caring it almost seemed to give the body life. After the preparations were finished, the body was draped in white sheets and placed in a basket made from palm leaves.

In the West dead people are usually avoided. Even the act of identifying a dead body is repulsive to many of us. And few would think of touching and caressing a corpse. In Bali, the cleaning, combing and touching of the body gives everyone an opportunity to say good-bye. There is nothing abhorrent or unclean about the dead person. Indeed, the person is treated with love and respect, and everyone is given an opportunity to pay their last respects with reverence.

In contrast, here in the West we distance ourselves from death, which creates problems for people who have lost loved ones. Many times the funeral is over so quickly and may seem so impersonal that mourners are left with the feeling that the person really didn't die or that they haven't really said good-bye. As a doctor, I have seen many patients who as children were not allowed to attend their parents' funerals and who feel angry and unresolved about their loved one's death.

UP IN SMOKE

The priest, regal in his long black beard and white robes, sat cross-legged on a high platform overlooking the body. The ceremony he performed took several hours. There were prayers and blessings, interspersed with chiming bells and sprinkling holy water on all of us gathered below.

Hindus believe that humans are composed of five elements: earth, wind, fire, ether and water. When a body is burnt it returns to these five elements. First it becomes fire and the ashes fall to the earth; the smoke then becomes vapors or ether, which is blown away by the wind. Finally the ashes are taken and thrown into the sea.

Just after sunset, when the prayers were finished, the women softly gathered the offerings and piled them high on their heads. The men lifted the huge bamboo platform with the funeral tower on top. The size of the platform and the number of tiers on the tower varies according to the caste of the

171

deceased. The higher the caste and the wealthier the person, then the larger and more elaborate the tower.

We all marched from the house, up alleyways, through the main street of the town, to the cremation field. The procession was followed by the whole orchestra playing gamelans, gongs, drums and flutes. Members of the village lined the streets and watched as we marched past stopping traffic in all directions.

At the cremation field, torches were lit and the body was ceremoniously removed from the tower and placed in a casket. Again the family brought food and drink, and said prayers. Finally a propane torch lit the platform and the body went up in flames. We saw the parts of the body burning, but it went very quickly compared with a ceremony I witnessed fourteen years previously when propane wasn't used. Still the smell of burning flesh permeated the air.

Now we were tired. We were driven back to our hotel by Agus and his wife. The family of the deceased waited until the fire was out, then headed for the nearest sea to spread the ashes. This custom is the final purification, the washing away of all uncleanliness. A number of days after the cremation, the Balinese hold a second funeral, which releases the body from all thought and feeling still clinging to it.

I was hesitant at first to have my three children attend this all-day celebration. I was concerned how they would react to death and was also worried they would get restless sitting around for eight hours. Surprisingly, the experience was a valuable one.

By witnessing the dead body and the way everyone related to it without the tears and screaming that sometimes goes on in the West, they could see the normality and acceptance of death as a natural part of life. They could look at the corpse without fear and seeing other people touching it, made it less scary. They became very curious, asking questions about where the brain goes after dying and why do we bury people in the ground. Allowing them to think of their own mortality helped put into perspective how lucky we were to be alive.

Larry, eleven at the time, was more disgusted when he watched one of the men sharpen a bamboo stick, slit the neck of a live chicken, and then drain the blood. David, who was seven, was fascinated by the fire and how the body burned, while Marc was surprised to see the naked body of the corpse, genitals exposed.

The Balinese cremation is a time for the family to come together to honor the departed. Everyone is busy with preparations, and the immediate family is supported and comforted. The home, rather than the funeral parlour or cemetery, becomes the central meeting place. Ritual and prayer is performed and everyone is touched in the process. For the one day at least, time stands still.

In Western countries, we are always fighting death, sometimes forgetting that everyone must die. We in the medical profession, through our desire to help, sometimes even keep patients alive with respirators, intravenous lines, and drugs long after the essence of the person is gone. Families sometimes suffer for weeks seeing their loved ones reduced to the "living dead" or are left feeling guilty that more could have been done.

Many people are comforted to know that their parent is buried in a grave they can visit. They don't like the idea that there is nothing left of the body. The Balinese feel the opposite. They believe that the soul lives on and resides in their family temple, and so they can communicate and feel the presence of their loved ones every day.

I left the cremation on a high. The energy of the ceremony calmed me and offered me a chance to slow down and contemplate death. There were no black costumes, but music, color and festivities. The Balinese's whole attitude toward death was so much healthier in every way than ours.

Given a choice, I think being a corpse in Bali would be a lot more fun!

MASS CREMATION

A few years later we were fortunate to take part in a mass cremation. Usually a cremation takes place as soon as money can be collected to pay for the festivities. However, if a family does not have the money, or there are not enough family members available to organize the event, then a mass cremation is performed about every five years.

More than a month's work went into the extraordinary cremation I attended in the village of Kedewatan, about five kilometres outside of Ubud. Included in the preparations was construction of huge bamboo platforms that touched the top leaves of the palm trees and elaborate wooden bulls, adorned with masks, standing 20 feet high. Baskets overflowing with mango, dates, and orchids were also made for each of the 30 people being honored at the cremation.

In the old days, the remains of these people would have been dug up from the ground, placed in a basket and carried in huge, wooden statues perched atop the elaborate bamboo platforms. However, the village counsel decided many years ago that graves could only be dug up symbolically and a symbol of the dead person would be used in their place.

The festivities began near dawn. Bonnie, Larry, David, Marc

174

and I arrived four hours later to see the huge wooden bulls lining the road, peering down at us from their platforms. Traffic was directed around these platforms and bamboo baskets were placed in the front. Hundreds of other baskets filled the entranceway to the temple.

Everyone was dressed in a black top and a black hat. Flashes of color came from the bright sarongs worn by both the men and women taking part in the celebration. Hundreds of villagers were crammed into the temple, weaving banana leaves and coconut palms for use in the ceremony.

We waited patiently for the festivities to begin, mingling with the crowds until finally at one o'clock the gamelan orchestra arrived — 20 men displaying special ceremonial cloth around their waists and heads. They sat cross-legged in front of their instruments and filled the air with the sound of music the entire day. After the first few songs, the priest, bearded and dressed in white, blessed everyone present.

After the prayers, about 15 men carried each of the heavy platforms two kilometers to the Pura Dalem, Temple of the Dead, on the outskirts of town. The pallbearers were in a light-hearted mood, turning and twisting the huge platforms, spinning them around and shouting as they walked along the road. Finally, the platforms were taken into the temple field and lined up on pyres. Hundreds of villagers flowed by in a long procession bearing offerings and making their way to the bull pyre where their kin was to be cremated.

The villagers walked around and around the pyre, symbolically feeding the spirit of the dead, making offerings and generally hovering by the platform. At four o'clock sticks and wood were put under each platform, then soaked with kerosene. A match was struck. The platforms went up in flames.

Men with large poles were standing by, turning the fire over. It was amazing to see this whole field full of burning pyres, filling the sky with smoke and bringing tears to our eyes. After the fires died down, relatives gathered around the ashes and searched for coins and other trinkets that had survived the flames. The ashes were later taken to the river and, in another ceremony, thrown into the water.

Although many of the deceased had died a number of years before, they had not been forgotten. The communal funeral was an excellent way to ensure that everyone, including people who had no money and few family members, would be honored. Funerals in North America seem rushed in comparison. It was a day we will never forget.

GALUNGAN-HERE COME OUR ANCESTORS

After giving a lecture at the International Congress on Traditional Medicine and Medicinal Plants, we decided to stay on to take part in one of the Bali's most important celebrations, Galungan.

On Galungan the deified ancestors of every family descend to their former homes where they must be welcomed with prayers and offerings. Since every Hindu household in Bali has a family temple, everyone returns to their family home to honour the spirits of their deceased relatives.

Putu, a waiter we met in Ubud, had invited me to attend an early-morning slaughter on the day before Galungan. I woke up at 4:30 a.m. to the sounds of a gentle rain, put on my sarong and walked up Monkey Forest Road in pitch blackness to visit with Putu.

A large, sad, pig lay tied to a bamboo pole as 10 men gath-

176

ered around. They were the caretakers of the gamelan and had purchased the pig together. Once slaughtered it would be divided equally among each family. First, the pig's mouth was tied with a piece of bamboo to muffle its screams. Next, while the 10 men held the pig down, a man with a large knife slit its throat and spilled its blood. Afterward, ashes saturated with kerosene were spread over the pig's body and set on fire to kill any germs and clean away any dirt. Then, the pig was scrubbed clean with bricks and water before it was cut up into equal shares.

The Balinese believe that their ancestors' spirits come back on Galungan to offer them guidance and protection during the upcoming year. The spirits stay around all week while special ceremonies and prayers are performed in their honour.

On the day of Galungan special food was prepared and we were invited to join Putu and his family for their mid-day meal. We also wanted to honour the spirit of this holy day in our own way, so we went to the small temple in our rented home and summoned the spirit of our ancestors. We talked about my dead father, uncles, aunts and Bonnie's grandparents. We tried to give our three children a sense of these relatives as unique individuals who touched our lives.

Bonnie and I have often thought of writing a spiritual will, not listing our material possessions but explaining to our children the beliefs we hold dear. We want to tell them about the importance of family, honesty, compassion, God, and other spiritual issues. This would be our real legacy.

We used our time at the temple to explain this and our children listened without interruption. They seemed to respond to the special nature of our communion.

177

BLESSED AND HEALED

One week after Galungan everyone visits their village temple and brings offerings as part of a celebration called Kuningan. On this special day the spirits are ushered back to the spirit world.

We were driven by our friends, Dr. Luh Ketut Suryani and her husband Dr. Tjok Alit, to Klungkung, a city that was once the centre of the Gelgel Dynasty, one of the most powerful kingdoms in Bali. Here we participated in a purification ceremony performed by one of the high priests.

As part of the ceremony we were sprinkled with holy water, bathed from the waist up, and blessed with flowers and prayers sung by the high priest. This delightful, smiling, bald-headed elder sat on a platform, cross-legged for hours, performing the ceremony on hundreds of followers.

After we were purified, Dr. Suryani took us to a traditional healer named Wayan Genah, who specialized in removing black magic curses that made people sick. He examined me and diagnosed that I had been possessed by some minor spirits. With a metal object wedged painfully between my fingers, Genah drew out the bad spirits from my body. He seemed to enjoy watching me squirm with pain. I'm not sure if he was a masochist or just happy that the bad spirits were leaving?

To finish off this amazing day, we went to Timrah Temple in Klungkung to observe a special trance ceremony. Ancestral spirits are housed in thatched, wooden, spirit boxes and returned to the temple to enable them to make their way back to the spirit world. These spirit boxes rested on platforms supported by huge bamboo ladders. Each of the 10 heavy platforms was carried by about 10 shirtless male villagers. They lead a large procession from the temple to the river and then, after a special ceremony, from the river back up to the temple courtyard.

There was a problem though. Apparently the spirits had been having too good a time among the people and, having a mind of their own, bucked at the thought of reentering the temple. Each time the men carrying these long bamboo platforms approached the temple entrance, some of the men carrying the ladder were prevented from climbing the stairs by agitated spirits.. The other men struggled and tried to force the platforms up the steep, narrow stone steps. In the chaos that followed the spirit boxes were spun around and around the temple courtyard by the men who put themselves into trance for the special occasion.

The atmosphere was frenzied for about an hour while the men, pushed, pulled and dragged the platforms around, seemingly out of control, knocking over anyone who got in the way of the whirling bamboo structures. Finally, amid the shrieking crowd and the throbbing music, ceremonial swords or krisses were brandished driving the spirits up the stairs and through the temple door.

Dr. Suryani, a professor of psychiatry at Udayana Medical School, explained that the Balinese are very controlled individuals and rarely show emotion in public. The trance, which is part of many ceremonies and dances, allows their pent-up emotions to surface. While in a trance men cry out, fall down, run amok and act crazy but not in a dangerous way. They feel like they are overtaken completely by the spirits and therefore are not responsible for their behavior. But it is rare for anyone in a trance to be hurt or harmed by another person. The goal is to release the stresses and strains of everyday life.

179

I know that even as an observer to this emotionally charged ceremony, I felt relieved and refreshed afterwards.

BALI HO?

It is the culture and way of life just as much as the cheap prices, beautiful beaches and sublime climate that attracts tourists. Anyone who is interested can take part in ceremonies, festivals, and religious events. The Balinese welcome visitors. But something gets lost in the sharing. What is the price tag on Balinese culture? Can a country sell its culture and still maintain it?

In their dances, paintings, shadow puppet plays and in their religious life there is a balance between good and evil. The Balinese constantly work to maintain this balance between the life-giving and the destructive forces. I was raised to believe that good would win out in the end. But the Balinese don't expect a triumph of either one. Both demonic and heavenly forces are catered to and accepted as part of the cosmic order.

So it is with tourism. Tourism brings employment, capital investments, an upgrading of daily life, more opportunities and stimulates their creative genius. However I tend to see the down side. As each area of Bali is touched by foreigners, the community turns away from traditional paths and looks to making money from the rich tourists. This plays havoc with family and village life. Young people seem to pick up the worst of Western traits. Violence, drugs, blue jeans, loud music are just some of the contaminating influences.

It's not just the people and their culture that is being hurt. So is the land. The forests are being destroyed indiscriminately, and the rivers, beaches and oceans are now polluted for the first time in the country's history.

Bali is a communal society that is held together by a sense of collective responsibility and sharing that permeates everything the people do. This collective responsibility puts considerable pressure on individuals to conform to traditional customs and values. If Bali is to retain its culture and its quality of life it the midst of thousands of tourists, it will be because of its belief in family and community.

The commitment to spiritual awareness, attention to ritual, and their acknowledgment of God in every aspect of life is a firm foundation. The respect for their elders, and reverence for their ancestors helps maintains order. Lastly, their connection to nature and their creativity help to preserve the richness of their culture.

But the struggle for balance continues. This sun-drenched, spiritual island has withstood the impact of Islam, which took over the rest of Indonesia beginning in the 13th century. It has withstood rampant Dutch colonialism from 1882 to 1942 and the Japanese occupation that took place from 1942 to 1945. Now it is facing its greatest challenge. Can it preserve its culture and way of life against the hordes of tourists looking for cheap beer, surfing and an escape from the urban jungle? Can it maintain its culture with the onslaught of refugees from various parts of troubled Indonesia?

SULAWESI: WHERE YOU LIVE TO DIE

Sulawesi, formerly known as Celebes, is an odd-shaped Indonesian island some 227,000 square kilometres in area, which makes it a little smaller than England and Scotland combined. At the time we visited, it had about 13 million inhabitants from hundreds of diverse cultures, the largest groups of which are the Bugis, the Makassarese, the Minuhasans, the Mandanese, the Chinese and the Torajans. The Torajans, who had a population of roughly 330,000, are primarily Christian. Most of Sulawesi, on the other hand, are Moslem.

Torajaland is nestled among the Central Highlands of South Sulawesi. This out-of-the way spot is cheap, has stunning landscapes, a fascinating culture and friendly natives.

Most tourists who visited Torajaland landed in Ujung Padang, Sulawesi's largest city, formerly known as Makassa. Although some people use Ujung Padang as a base to explore the coral islands, waterfalls, caves and communities to the east and south, most visitors quickly pass through the city. They stay overnight and catch an early morning plane, or ride overland to Tana Toraja.

While in Ujung Padang, it is enjoyable to take a stroll along Pantai Losari, the esplanade; watch the many sea-fairing vessels, called Prahu, from the mouth of the harbour; and explore Fort Rotterdam, a waterfront fortress built by the Dutch in the late seventeenth and eighteenth centuries; walk in the shadows of temples and churches; meander along Jalan Sombaopu; and duck into shops filled with carvings, antiques and trinkets from the far away islands of Irian Jaya, Kalimantan, Flores and Bali.

We decided to travel overland to Toraja by car and take a

plane back. The eight-hour trip has scenery that you won't see anywhere else in the world. Our journey transported us over 130 kilometers of narrow coastline dominated by limestone ridges, endless rice patties and picturesque towns with bustling markets. We stopped for lunch at Pare, the second largest port in South Sulawesi.

Then the road turned inland, winding its way through rice fields and stunning mountains with panoramic views around each curve. We glimpsed banana, papaya and bamboo trees; traversed mulberry fields and clove plantations; then went down, down into the Makale and Rantepao Valleys. Along the way we saw natives going about their daily business: farming rice, carrying water, tending water buffalo. There was also a constant stream of school children bedecked in their blue uniforms.

THE HIGHLIGHT OF ONE'S LIFE IS DEATH

Every society deals with death in its own way. The funeral and burial rites of the Torajans are quite strange by most standards and it is this oddity that draws thousands of tourists to the area. The funeral is a four-day event, depending on the person's caste or rank in society. There are three classes: nobles, commoners and slaves. Where you belong determines the extent of the ritual and the grandness of the ceremony. The higher up the caste you go the greater the obligations put upon you and your family.

The rituals surrounding death, which involve many other previous animistic religious practices, have survived the influence of Christianity. All Torajan funerals are intended to transport the soul to the next world. They are also intended to free survivors from the deceased. When a person dies, they are wrapped in cloth and kept in the house for months — even years — while preparations are made for the funeral. Only after the ceremony is finished is the corpse considered dead. Before that, the body is attended to as if it were a sick person.

The funeral takes place after enough money is found and arrangements are made for relatives to come from all over Indonesia and outside to attend the funeral. Often people work a lifetime just to pay for the funerals of their family.

On the first day of the funeral, people come together to chant and pray. Guests arrive in a procession, leading water buffalo and toting pigs, rice packets, palm wine and other gifts. Ritual fields, lined with temporary shelters of bamboo and straw, are home to the guests. Animals given to the family represent debts eventually to be paid back. As a tourist, I was told to bring sugar or cigarettes as a gift. Can you imagine how difficult it was for me, a physician, to bring a box of cigarettes to the funeral? But custom and respect prevailed over preventative medicine.

Small animal offerings include chickens and pigs, but large offerings, primarily water buffalo, are also made. A water buffalo is a special gift. It becomes a debt of the family who receives it. That debt is repaid when there is a funeral in the giver's family. The Torajan people believe that a person's status and successful passage to the hereafter is faster and better, the more water buffalo that are slaughtered in their honour. Also, the larger the festival and the more people attending, the better the afterlife.

We were lucky to attend a large funeral of an elderly matron who died in her 70s in the mountain village of Londo, 25 kilometers north of Rantepao. Our driver took us over a barely passable mountain road, littered with rocks, holes and debris. The road was just wide enough for our car.

When we arrived at Londo there were at least 15 vehicles parked near the village, all carrying tourists. A thatched village had been built for the funeral. In the centre of the village, swaying slightly, were 20 to 30 water buffalo. Hundreds of people sat around in huts, while others stood and watched. We were invited into the dead person's family area where we were offered cookies and coffee. And we waited.

Water buffalo are everywhere in Torajaland. They all have a rope through their nose and can be found tied up in fields, rivers, rice patties, and front yards. They are treated well, cleaned and cared for. They are also completely docile. It is considered a great honour for the animal to be slaughtered for this ceremony.

Much to our surprise, although we were forewarned, one buffalo after another was brought forward for sacrificing. In each case one of the animal's legs was tied to a post in the ground. A young man held its head up by tugging on the rope in its nose. Then with a sharp machete, he slashed deep into the neck. Blood gushed from the wound, the animal jumped and kicked, falling to the ground. The buffalo died in front of our eyes.

Twelve buffalos were slaughtered amid shouts and cries from the crowd. The tourists turned green. The young men with the knives looked proudly at the dead buffalo scattered in heaps in the village. No sooner had the animals been killed than men began skinning them, dividing up the meat among the various families present.

This was only the first day of the funeral. Many more buffalo were slaughtered the next day. We were shocked at the violence and the blood. The animals seemed to suffer tremendously but the crowd enjoyed the excitement. There was also an element of danger; we never knew if a buffalo would break free and hurt a bystander. I wanted to capture the event on film so I witnessed each killing, refusing to turn away. Maybe the camera was just an excuse for me to watch the violence.

Seeing these animals slaughtered — painfully — reminded us again of the high cost of eating meat. When we sat down to our next meal and saw a buffalo steak as one of the choices, we opted for a vegetarian meal. In fact, we didn't eat meat for quite some time thereafter. I'm convinced that if we want to convince people to eat less meat, cut back on animal fat, and move toward a vegetarian diet, we should have public slaughterhouses where everyone must watch animals being killed at least once a week.

After one or two days of this ritualistic slaughter, the human body was carried in a procession to nearby cliffs or caves. Holes were carved out of rocks and the corpse was placed inside. The grave was later sealed. Towtows, carved wooden likenesses of the dead person, were placed outside the burial site. These effigies blessed and watched over the deceased.

In Toraja, infants who die before teething are placed in cavities cut into the trunk of a tree. The hole is then sealed so the tree can grow around the infant, who becomes part of its spirit.

After the half day we spent at the funeral in Londo, we were driven to Locomoto where we saw cliff graves. We were dropped off near this mountain village and set out on a three-hour trek down the mountain. Our afternoon hike was filled with unforgettable views of the mountains and the valley below. We were well off the beaten track and had an opportunity to see the way the locals lived. We passed through villages and rice fields. Everywhere we went we were followed by children calling out for candies, yelling "Hello. Hello". We walked to the village of Panna and then to the village of Tikala, where we saw more rock and baby graves.

The next day we did touristy things. At Londo we saw burial sites in limestone cliffs and graves etched deep into caves. In Lemo, we saw the famous towtows that watch over the cliffside graves. At Ke'te'kesu', we became part of an ancient village with its long rows of traditional rice barns. The roofs of these barns are curved in the shape of a sailing vessel, symbolic of the boats that brought the settlers to this island thousands of years ago. At Suaya we saw more hanging graves, baby graves, coffins and bones.

Another highlight was white water rafting. With a tour company called Sobek, we were driven two nerve-racking hours up the mountain, across impassable roads in a four wheel drive Land Rover. We stayed overnight on straw mattresses in the home of the village chief and the next day hiked down to the Maulu River, a branch of the Sadan.

For the first hour or so the rapids were dangerous. We twirled and spun, madly rowing trying to follow our relaxed guide's instructions on how to avoid catastrophe. After the initial treachery, we settled down to a fairly lazy, meandering journey passing villages, water buffalo, rare birds and huge lizards. We had a picnic lunch on the river bank. At the end of the day, we were picked up at Baranam and taken to our hotel.

Sulawesi is such an isolated place that although we only spent a week, it seemed like we were gone much longer. The environment was just so different. Television, video games, computers, microwaves, and portable phones had not reached there yet. If you are looking for adventure, beautiful scenery, unique death rituals, and friendly natives, consider Sulawesi. Like in so many of the other cultures mentioned, tourism is rapidly altering the fabric of its society.

GOODBYE TO EASY RIDER ON SAMOSIR ISLAND

JOURNEY TO MEDAN

Ever since our first trip to Asia in 1975 we had always wanted to visit Lake Toba, the largest lake in South East Asia. But in order to fly to this remote beautiful area on the island of Sumatra, we had to stop in Medan, a large polluted city. Bonnie, our three sons and I flew from Bali to Jakarta in order to connect to Medan, but unfortunately, our plane to Medan was cancelled. We were forced to take a later flight that caused us to arrive in Medan too late to connect to Lake Toba in one day. Regrettably, we had to stay overnight in congested Medan.

Upon arrival at 9:30 PM, we took a taxi ride into the city, to one of the hotels that was recommended in the "Lonely Planet Guide Book". It was fully booked, so we went around the corner to a place that should have been called the "Hole-In-The-Ground Hotel."

HOTEL FROM HELL

By the time we got there it was 10:30 PM and the owner had us in an uncompromising position. It was too late to search for another place and from what we were told, there was no other place that was going to be any better. So as was customary in

189

Indonesia, we started to bargain for our rooms. The owner stood fast at 50,000 rupees, about $25.00 for two rooms. Our children looked exhausted and we thought one night would not kill us. Little did we know.

Each small, bland 8' x 10' room had white washed walls, with a tiny window facing a dirty wall, two feet away. There was a squeaky, double bed, a noisy fan on the side table, and a squatter for a toilet. A squatter, a familiar site in Asia, meant there was no toilet but merely a hole in the ground. You position your feet on either side of the hole and make your donation in a crouched down position. We rationalized that it was an excellent way to build up your thigh muscles and since no part of your body needs to contact any potentially infected toilet seat, in many ways it was more sanitary. You flush the toilet by pouring water from a hand held dipper that you fill from a basin beside the toilet.

To make matters worse, there was no toilet paper, soap or top sheet on the bed. Normally we had to bargain for these extra luxury items and usually the hotel owner would throw these extras in with the room. After ten minutes of arguing, he relinquished a towel for each room, but refused to give us soap, toilet paper or a top sheet. Fortunately we had battered toilet paper we had saved from Toronto just for this special occasion and soap we had salvaged from our last hotel.

It was hard for him to understand our custom of using toilet paper. The Asian way of wiping one's backside is by splashing water from a small hand-held dipper using one's left hand. You dip this little container into a mandy, which was like a small tub filled with water. Sometimes it could be just a pail of water sitting on the floor or a basin of water. After splashing your behind with water, you wipe the remaining faeces off using your left hand. Since often there was no way of drying, you kind of drip-dry your bum in the open air. This is why shaking a person's hand with your left hand or serving food with your left hand is considered an insult in Asia and the Middle East.

I never understood how splashing water was better than toilet paper. It always astounded me when I visited hospitals and doctor's offices, that they had no toilet paper. I often got into great dialogues with medical doctors about the benefits of tissue. Needless to say, times are a changing and there is more acceptance of toilet paper everywhere in the world.

The other major shortcoming was that the primitive shower in the children's room was continuously dripping. It could not be turned off and made such a loud trickling and splashing noise that I was afraid it was going to keep the boys awake all night. Close by the shower, the light switch to the washroom was hanging out of the wall by its electrical wires. This was a potentially dangerous situation. When we tried to ask our gruff, unfriendly hotel owner if he could do something about it, he said with a smile that everything was fine and it would still be 50,000 rupiah for two rooms. He reiterated that it was a great price and bragged about how it included break-fast for five people. This might seem like a wonderful extra option, but when I enquired further about breakfast, he proudly said it was coffee or tea and toast. I asked if there were any eggs, fruit salad or pancakes, as was the tradition in Indonesia. With a satisfied grin he said no.

We slept restlessly through a hot, humid, sauna-like night and were woken at five o'clock by the Muslim prayers at the huge beautiful Masjid Mosque down the road. All through Indonesia, modern mosques have minarets and loudspeaker systems which belt out prayers five times a day. Part of the joy of being in this area was getting up with the faithful.

MEDAN TO LAKE TOBA

To get to Lake Toba we had three choices. We could take the public bus, squished and crowded in with smokers, chickens and bunches of bananas. One never knows how many people or what kind of bus you could get. We had seen many of these buses overturned by the side of the road, so this was not our first option. Next, we could go by tourist bus, supposedly modern and fast with air conditioning, but it was a long trek of perhaps an hour to get to the bus terminal. The unanimous choice of our family was to phone a taxi for 70,0000 rupees, the equivalent of about $35.00 US.

The taxi was a big, old, 1950's Datsun, which reminded me of a cross between a boat, and a 1957 Chev. Effendi, the driver, did not speak a word of English. I got someone to translate that we did not want to go fast and wanted to stop along the way for photos. What we forgot to tell him was that we did not want to him to pass huge trucks by entering into the on-coming lanes of speeding motorcycles, cars and buses. Since we had difficulty explaining this, for the entire journey I was yelling and screaming from the front seat and repeatedly witnessing my life pass before my eyes. The back seat was like an old bed that sagged in the middle, with the springs poking into my family who were squished together like sardines.

Regrettably, the driver smoked those horrible Asian cigarettes that smelled worse than any cigar you have ever breathed. I did not want to argue or tell him to put it out because I feared he might get irritable and this might affect his high speed driving. I felt like Pavlov's dog. When I saw him pull out the cigarette from his shirt pocket I immediately became nauseous.

The three and a half hour taxi ride to Lake Toba was monotonous. We passed through the squalor of small Asian towns. We did pass some amazing rubber and palm tree plantations. Irreplaceable rainforest with endangered species were being cut down to make way for the big business of these plantations.

Finally we got to our destination Samosir Island, a wedge-shaped island in the middle of Lake Toba. The Batok, who are Christian and inhabit this island, were originally cannibal, head hunters. A week previously a ferry had capsized on Lake Toba and 200 people were killed so we were a little nervous about crowding onto the ferry. After a scenic forty-five minute boat ride we arrived safely on Samosir Island and got off at the area called Tuk Tuk, the peninsula where all the hotels were situated. There are no Hiltons or Sheratons here, but small, family run, inexpensive hotels where most travelers paid around $10.00 a room. We decided to splurge and got two rooms with real toilet seats and hot water at the Samosir Cottages.

Unfortunately, there still was no soap or toilet paper provided. We had to buy these in the market but luckily the hotel was willing to give us towels after we asked. The atmosphere was subdued, everything was cheap, and the people friendly. Tracy Chapman, and Bob Marley songs played in the restaurants. Everywhere there were signs for motorcycles for rent and magic mushrooms to eat. These psilocybin mushrooms attracted many travelers who were children of children of the 60's.

EASY RIDER

We rented two motorcycles for about ten dollars for the day. Bonnie and I sandwiched our twelve-year old son Marc, onto one motorcycle and Larry who was nineteen and David fifteen rode on the other. It took a while, but eventually Larry learned how to work the brake and gears while balancing the bike. These were the worst roads we had ever seen. There were huge potholes everywhere and bridges that were improperly patched with sticks and slabs of wood, leaving large gaping holes. By the side of the road there were pretty flowers, chickens, roosters, pigs, and even some beautiful yellow birds. The most common road kill were baby chicks.

The 45 km. journey began by our children singing "Born to be Wild". The road was spotted with churches and cemeteries. We passed water buffalo meandering across the road; goats playing and head butting each other; huge herons sitting in trees and fairly quiet dogs. Our destination was the Panguran Hot Springs halfway across the island. The amazing underground spring fed a swimming pool and therapeutic baths. Surprisingly it took us three and a half hours and by the time we got to the Hot Springs, we were tired. We walked around and swam in the hot pool. When we got back on our motorcycles to make the drive home, we realized too late that it was getting dark, and we were exhausted.

Then came the big trauma of the trip. About half way home, Larry crashed his motorcycle in a huge pothole. The bike fell on his leg causing not only a burn and a gash to his inner thigh but a large oozing wound just above his ankle. The bike was broken, and we did not know how to fix it. Locals came by to try to help us out. After a number of attempts and a crowd of about fifteen people, one gentleman finally figured out what was wrong and put the motorcycle back together. We bravely hopped back onto the cycles and continued on our way. We were getting a bit concerned because it started to rain just as the sun was setting.

We thankfully arrived almost in one piece and gave the bikes back to the owner, not sure what consequences would befall us. We had heard horror stories of other tourists who were ripped off for hundreds of dollars for relatively minor repairs. Fortunately the man who rented it to us was not a thief. He took the bike to a repair shop to get a written estimate and presented us with a bill for 65,000 rupees, about thirty dollars.

It was an unforgettable journey. We saw some incredible scenery and my son, who had always wanted to buy a motorcycle and travel across Canada, had the Easy rider dream knocked out of him. Smashing up his leg was a small price to pay for the wisdom of the dangers of a motorcycle.

MAN OF THE FOREST-BUKIT LAWANG

Tarzan has always been was one of my favourite stories. The notion that man and apes have similar origins made sense to me. Instead of just seeing them locked in cages in a zoo, I always wanted to see monkeys living in the wild, to confirm my belief that Homo sapiens and orang-utans share a common mammalian genogram. The fact that orang-utans are becoming extinct as their habitats are being destroyed made me want to see them before they were entirely wiped out.

We had to drive back to Medan and then take a two and a half hour taxi ride to the village of Bukit Luwang and the Bohorok Orang-utan Conservation Centre. Located on the banks of the Bohorok River, Bukit Lawang exists only for the Conservation Centre and most tourists stay overnight in one of

the small hotels built on the edge of the river.

The Rehabilitation Centre, supported by the Frankfort Zoological Society, was founded by Regina Frey and Monica Borner in 1973. Bohorok is only a small part of the huge Mt. Leuser National Park, a rainforest housing some of the most endangered and rare species on earth. These two women conceived of the idea of rescuing orang-utans from their destroyed habitats and confinement as household pets and releasing them into the wild in a protected manner.

Orang-utans are huge, gentle, ape-like creatures with human mannerisms. They are extremely intelligent, amazingly agile and peaceful, never attacking humans. They live almost exclusively in the high ancient trees of the rain forests. Sumatra's rainforest was systematically being destroyed, and the wood was exported to other Asian countries like Japan. Rainforests were also being cleared to make way for farms, as well as rubber and palm tree plantations. As the trees were destroyed the orang-utans became homeless. The devastation had been brought to the public eye because the fires used to clear the forests were creating smoke that was blanketing all of South-East Asia, affecting people's health and badly affecting the tourist industry.

Workers from the Orang-utan Conservation Centre are called in as a forest is being destroyed to try to capture the orang-utans before the last tree of their habitat is cut down. With a team of about 10 men and nets they climb up higher than the orang-utans, and force them down to where other huge nets capture them. Taken to the Conservation Centre and kept in quarantine for six weeks to make sure they are free of disease, they are then given shots, have chest x-rays, before being eventually released into Mt. Leuser National Park.

Very often orang-utans are illegally captured and put in cages as pets. Many have been in cages so long they forgot or never learned how to climb. After they are turned into the Centre they are taught the basics of natural living such as tree climbing, making a nest for resting and sleeping and avoidance of touching the ground.

The caged animals don't know how to take care of themselves and during the first few weeks or months as they are taught how to adjust, they are fed twice a day at the feeding station. The feeding station is basically a large wooden platform high up in the trees in the middle of the jungle where the staff from the Centre give out bananas and milk. The orang-utans that are kept in cages are walked over to be fed and others that are living in the wild visit to pick up the food. The diet of milk and bananas is particularly monotonous to stimulate the formerly captive creatures to search for food on their own in the forest. Once they are able to live independently they are taken far off into the forest and forced to live fully on their own.

In order to visit the feeding station it was necessary to pick up a day permit at the Indonesian Nature Conservation Office (PAPA). There were two feedings each day at 8:00 am and 3:00 pm and most tourists came to witness the feedings. The walk to the feeding station was a difficult one. It took about 45 minutes to walk the 2 km. hike from the village up the river to the river crossing. The orang-utan feeding station is located on the other side of the river and the only way to get across is in an old dug out canoe(prahu).

We waited in line for about 20 minutes while they loaded nine tourists at a time into the canoe and walked it across the river to the other side. At the other side there was a steep, very difficult uphill 300 meter trek to the feeding station. It was so hot even at

6:30 in the morning that we were soaked in sweat by the time we arrived. We had the delightful opportunity to walk from the compound with a couple of orang-utans who weren't yet independent. It was just like walking with a couple of toddlers.

We stood in awe of these amazing animals as they swung in, from all directions, picked up their bananas and milk and kind of looked at us as we looked at them. It wasn't exactly clear if we were there to see them or they had come to see the funny humans all huddled together, watching them dine. We stood with about forty people from all over the world. There were so many cameras and photos snapped that it looked like a Kodak commercial. Everyone was gently pushing and vying to get a good view. The whole thing was quite contrived and artificial. Yet it was a special experience, to be so close to these huge animals and yet so safe. We felt like voyeurs.

Services of guides can be arranged at the National Park office for a few hours, half a day, a full day or longer. You must be accompanied by a guide whenever you go for a jungle walk within the National Park area. We went on a all day hike with a guide into the jungle and saw orang-utans in the wild, a family of gibbons, hundreds of large ants, termites, all kinds of beautiful birds and huge trees. The 200 year-old trees were my favourite.

I was saddened to know that these ancient forests were being decimated and the orang-utans exterminated. Once ranging throughout Southeast Asia, the species occupies only small pockets of habitat on the islands of Borneo and Sumatra. Their fate is tied to the Malaysian and Indonesia people whose land they share. But it also depends on global economics that drive the wood market as well as the demand for illegal pets.

Bukit Lawang is a small ray of hope in an otherwise pessimistic future. It is well worth the long journey to Sumatra.

DEVELOPING A PLANE PHOBIA IN IRIAN JAYA

We knew flying to Irian Jaya was going to be difficult, but we could never have predicted what an adventure we would have. Irian Jaya, the other half of Papua New Guinea, is an Indonesian island famous for its primitive societies who until recently, had never been in contact with modern civilization. Few tourists visit this area because it is so difficult to reach. A few days before we began our journey to Irian Jaya, a Merpati Airlines plane had crashed and so to begin with we were a little bit nervous.

We left the Orang-utan Conservation Centre just after breakfast and drove three hours to the airport in Medan. From Medan we flew to Jakarta and after a six hour delay took a connecting flight to Ujang Padang on the island of Sulawesi. Then another connecting flight took us to Biak before going on to Jayapura, the main town in Irian Jaya. All in all it took us twenty four hours and we arrived exhausted and shell-shocked.

We were told not to waste time in Jayapura because it had nothing to offer except for deadly falciparam malaria. Our destination was Wamena a 45 minute flight into the isolated interior highlands, but we had to stop in Jayapura to get "surat jalan" or walking papers to visit the Dani tribes.

I first attempted to get the "surat jalan" at the police station at the Sentani Airport where we landed. But the officers told me I had to go to Jayapura, 24 kilometres away. At first I tried a small public bus, squished in a van with sixteen smoking natives, a few chickens, bunches of bananas and bags of rice. I quickly realized it wasn't going to work so I jumped out and searched for a taxi. Getting a taxi at the side of the road wasn't easy but eventually Bam Bang came along driving an old red van with passengers already in the back seat.

200

When Bam Bang told me it was going to take an hour to get to Jayapura and of course, another hour back, I disappointedly realized that we were going to miss the flight to Wamena and might have to stay overnight in Jayapura, a malaria-infested waste of time.

In Jayapura, at the police station, I hurried to the office for foreign visitors but the man who handled the "surat jalan" was of course out for lunch.

"Please officer, could you hurry. My family is waiting at the airport, we have to catch a flight and we have to leave urgently," I pleaded.

He was not impressed. When the official came back from lunch, I had to give him our passports and two passport photos for each of my family. He sent me to a copy shop, just outside the police station, to get 10 copies of the passports. Every time you visit a different village in the Baliem Valley you have to leave a copy with the police.

An hour later, I watched the thin, slow moving, government official type up each document on an old 1950's typewriter. I paid 20,000 rupees, or about 10 dollars, and took the hour-long taxi ride back to the airport. I found my family angry from the long hot wait, surrounded by a crowd of locals, all hustling them for one thing or another. Some wanted them to stay at their hotel; others wanted them to buy trinkets; while others wanted to be their guide in Wamena. Unfortunately our flight had left.

FINDING A FLIGHT

Even though my family was frustrated and upset, I said goodbye once more and took off with Bam Bang to find a way of getting to Wamena so we would not have to stay in Jayapura.

201

We tried Airfast Airlines, the Missionary Airline, Merpati and Sempati Airlines, but to no avail. It was then my driver told me about Tirangi Airlines.

Tirangi was essentially a cargo outfit, which often took passengers. I squeezed through a hole in a locked gate, only to find a big warehouse full of all kinds of cargo. I hesitantly went over to the makeshift wooden office and asked for information but no one spoke English. With the help of my driver we figured out we could leave later that day to Wamena for the price of 132,000 rupees a person, a little bit more than we paid for the scheduled Merpati flight, we had missed.

FEAR OF FLYING

Hours later, we watched them load a small propeller Folker 16. We didn't realize we climbed up the back stairs to board the plane, just how dilapidated and disgusting this aircraft looked.

In Indonesia rules and regulations for how things are supposed to be kept, are not strictly enforced. Over time things deteriorate. This was true with hotels, bridges, hospitals, but we did not expect the same with airlines. The whole plane was filled with hundreds of burlap sacks, one on top of each other, with a net holding them all in place. Two seats, which had been removed to make space for the cargo, were perched on top of the bags, totally free, and not even tied down.

The emergency exit door through which we boarded didn't seem to want to shut and people outside kept slamming the door trying to get it closed. But it just didn't seem to fit. The airplane employers were laughing and saying, "Don't worry, don't worry".

I screamed, "Of course you don't have to worry. You are not on this plane."

The floor was covered in plywood, the seats were all ripped, the trays were unlockable, and many were taped shut with duct tape. That magical invention duct tape was unfortunately used to keep many of the inside parts of the filthy plane together.

Then came the big decision- should we just leave now and save our lives or should we take this flight with the risk that the five of us could go up in smoke. We already paid for our tickets and it would be difficult getting our money back. We wanted to get to Wamena, and couldn't picture the five of us debarking, marching across the runway, getting our two bags off the plane, telling them that we were too frightened and wanted our money back.

Scared out of my pants, I tried not to show my horror to our three children, but even they could tell that this was going to be a problem aircraft. There was no life vest under the seats; they were having difficulty locking the door; the men were laughing; the washroom was abominable, and there was no soap. Normally when you get on a flight, 'the no smoking sign' goes on. Not only was there no 'no smoking sign', but as soon as we took off the pilot and people in the cockpit started chain smoking. The whole aircraft quickly became filled up with smoke.

Throughout that journey we were praying to every religion we could think of. My young son Marc kept yelling, "We're all going to die. We're all going to die."

He kept giving us excerpts from the movie "Alive". The pilots invited our sons to come to the cockpit. They climbed over the cargo to the front of the plane. David noticed that it was a Nigerian Airlines plane that was built in 1969. This was not reassuring. It was a long, adrenalin- charged, rapid heart rate, forty-five minute flight. When we finally landed we cheered, danced and laughed. The pilot took a video of us, perhaps never seeing tourists so happy to be alive.

Our flight was a perfect example of how paranoia can get the best of you. Irian Jaya was well worth the long journey and the fear. Needless to say when it came time to fly home we didn't take Tirangi Airlines.

MOUNTAIN CLIMBING IN IRIAN JAYA – PENIS GOURDS AND GRASS SKIRTS

My Yuppie wife, our three Guppy children and I are not really mountain climbers. We like to walk, but we don't get an endorphin rush from hiking. After some adventurous friends of ours visited the Baliem Valley on the island of Irian Jaya and told us about the vanishing primitive culture of the Dani tribes we were curious enough to put in our orthotics and lace up our walking shoes.

The Dani people live in central Irian Jaya, and were only "discovered" by the rest of the world in the last 50 years. Indonesia partitioned Irian Jaya in 1945 and has been less than sensitive to the ways and culture of these primeval people.

The natives remind me of the aborigines in the outback of Australia. They are quiet, friendly, and live extremely simple lives. When they meet you, they greet you with a long hand-shake, gaze into your eyes and hang out with you, holding your hand for 30 seconds to a minute. The contact is quite intense and the experience feels all encompassing. They seem to be living totally in the moment, with all the time in the

world to say hello. When you meet them, you experience the quiet of their minds.

You can get so caught up in the greeting that you might fail to notice that the majority of the men are completely naked except for a gourd covering their penis. The gourd, a hollowed out vegetable, shaped like an elongated squash, fits over their manhood and is held up by a string attached around their waist. The women are also naked except for a grass skirt slung low on the hip. The women carry all their worldly belongings in woven baskets slung across their foreheads and hanging down their backs.

We spent the first three days gaining our confidence by going on day trips in the valleys, filled with beautiful scenery, leisurely paced hiking and no sign of danger. We decided to be more adventurous and try a two-day trek up a mountain, sleeping overnight in an isolated primitive village in the mountains.

We had been staying at the best hotel in Wamena, the Baliem Palermo Hotel. Each room cost about $30.00 a night including breakfast. There was no hot water but they did provide a Western toilet, toilet paper, towels, a sheet and blanket on the bed and soap, which was luxurious compared to some of the other so called hotels in town. These features made the "Palace" as it was so proudly called, almost rate as a one star hotel. We were especially grateful that they were willing to spray the room just before sunset to eliminate most of the mosquitoes. Irian Jaya is feared for it's dangerous strain of malaria falciparum. I had recurrent nightmares of dreaded mosquitoes with their huge proboscises biting into my defenceless children and newspaper headlines of "doctor's kids die of falciparum malaria".

Our plan was to hire a guide who we thought might take along a porter to carry our things. We were surprised to discover a party of five to help us on our journey. Our guide Mal, a five-foot smiling Dani native, had shopped the night before and bought the food that we would need. One porter carried our knapsack, containing all the clothes for our family of five. Another porter carried the majority of the food, while another carried the eggs and fragile foods like fruit. Mal's wife, our cook, carried our three large bottles of water and a carton of cheap cigarettes that we would use as gifts along our journey. Her sister who helped with the cooking, carried our sleeping mats and two flimsy blankets they had purchased at the local store.

We hired a beat up old antique car to take us one bumpy hour south of Wamena. There at the end of the road, was our embarkation point, a small town named Kurima. Mal took our walking papers and some money to the police to get permission for our trek.

From Kurima we walked straight up the imposing mountain, huffing and puffing, and resting every 15-20 minutes or so to catch our breath. As we climbed higher, we could see all across the immense Baliem Valley to the incredible mountain ranges on all sides. The raging Baliem River below was winding its way to the Baliem Gorge.

Dotted along the slope of the mountains were terraced fields growing mostly taro and sweet potato. In the distance we could see tiny, primitive villages clinging to the mountainside. All along our journey we were greeted by Dani men, naked except for their penis gourds, and women smiling hello as they passed. Children with snotty noses, large bellies suffering from kwashiorkor (protein deficiency) would tag along asking for sweets.

Each village we came to had an identical arrangement of round thatched huts. One hut housed the women and children. Another separate hut was for the men. Another hut was used as the kitchen and one more hut housed the pigs, their most valuable possession. If a man wanted to have sex with his wife, then he would visit his wife's hut usually in the middle of the night.

I became enamoured by the multitude of pigs everywhere. We saw them lying in mud, digging up roots, snorting and being caressed by the locals. Every time I tried to get close to pet one of the cute critters, they scurried away. Pigs were given as a dowry to obtain a wife. The average price for a bride was ten pigs and multiple wives were not uncommon. I often thought that with the cash I had on hand, I could pick up a wife or two to take back to Toronto. What stopped me was that I'm sure they would never have tolerated our Canadian winters.

Around mid-day we stopped on a slope by a little stream to have lunch. Immediately crowds of children and other naked tourist gazers huddled around us. The children were sadly malnourished and covered in flies. Our guide sang African sounding native songs while the women built a fire and cooked cabbage, potatoes and carrots for lunch. We had the luxury of tangerines and pineapple for dessert. To add to the strangeness of this mountain scene, one of the locals was completely naked, strolling along strumming a hand carved ukulele and singing native folk songs. He reminded me of Pete Seeger without clothes.

The views of the valley from our position high up in the clouds were spectacular. The highlight was the panoramic scene of the Baliem Gorge. The clouds were shifting and moving, so that we could get glimpses of the mountaintops hidden behind. We had hiked an entire day and as sunset approached, we descended a steep vertical slope, almost 250 meters straight down to the village of Tangma.

Tangma was built on a plateau in the middle of the huge mountain. When we arrived just before sunset, thirty or so children gathered round with curiosity, to greet our sons. They were particularly fascinated by my son David's braces. Their eyes nearly popped out of their heads when he opened his mouth and showed his teeth. They had never seen steel on someone's teeth before. They would have fainted if they knew how much his orthodontist bill cost.

They developed a game of chase and run. The children would assemble, stare at David, who would grit his teeth and shout. They would run away screaming in fear and he would chase them. The chase and scare game went on for about an hour, back and forth, until darkness set in.

We were given the luxury of sleeping in an old wooden shack with four rooms. It was large and lavish by their standards. The kitchen housed an open fire on a dirt floor. Another room had a wooden table with benches where we ate our supper. We were honoured with the only bedroom which had a wooden platform bed with a foul looking, crumbling piece of foam mattress covered by a grimy blanket.

We decided that all of us would sleep on the filthy floor on top of straw mats that our guide had purchased. As we entered the room that was destined to be our bedroom, Bonnie and I saw a large rat with an endless tail sitting on the windowsill. We knew it wasn't going to be a restful night. We decided to keep our little rat secret from our children. We were scared enough.

Delaying going to sleep as long as possible, we huddled together using our sarongs and towels as blankets and clothes as pillows. We worried about mosquitoes, malaria and the possibility of rats nibbling on our toes or ears. As I lay on the hard, uncomfortable floor in total darkness, I kept watch with my ears wide open. Every little sound made me squirm with the image of rats closing in.

The toilet was a tiny, squalid, smelly room with a hole in the floor. There was no running water, just a barrel of water with a ladle. After peeing and pooping you filled the ladle and poured the water down the hole washing the waste away. The strategy was to take a deep breath in and do your business. If you ran out of breath then holding one's nose was the next best thing. Luckily we brought our own toilet paper because otherwise there was none.

When we left the next morning, we had to climb the hardest part of our trek, straight up the mountain. We rested at various spots to catch our breath and looked back to the remarkable scene of the valley below, where we had spent the night. All along the path, we waved at and greeted the friendly Dani people. We passed patches of taro, traditional villages neatly tucked on the mountain plateaus and finally descended again down to the river where we made our camp for lunch. After, we hiked down to the raging Baliem River we murmured a sigh of relief, thankful that the trek was over and we had survived. We took a taxi home relieved to be at our one star hotel with it's real toilet, firm bed and cold running water.

The trek was one of life's highlights. We sweated, panted, and struggled up and down a mountain and we had a chance to visit a vanishing way of life. We were impressed that our kids never once complained and our children were impressed that their middle-aged yuppie parents could still climb mountains.

CHAPTER SIXTEEN
INDIA – GOA, KASHMIR

GO TO GOA BEFORE GOA IS GONE

I missed Woodstock because I was traveling on $5.00 a day through Europe that summer. For those of you who are too young or too old to remember Woodstock, besides being a movie, a song and a town, it was a "happening" where almost half a million young people from across the United States came for a weekend of rock music to a farm near Woodstock, New York. They celebrated life, love, and peace in the last major "BE-IN" of the hippie generation.

Now, I was a "closet hippie" which really converts nicely to a modern Yuppie. If I put on my faded blue jeans, sandals, singlet and got into the right "head space" I could identify with the "us" generation. Sometimes I was even called a hippie by unsuspecting and nondiscriminating children in foreign countries.

Since I still believe in Ram Das, the Beatles, non-intercourse free love, and Crosby, Stills, Nash and Young, I wanted to get back to the place, to try and set my soul free.

I was invited to attend the First International Conference on Unani Medicine in New Delhi, India. After giving a lecture on traditional healing and spending three days learning about herbal remedies, Islam, and pulse diagnosis, Bonnie and I felt we needed a holiday, and Goa was the best choice. Apparently Goa is the place where the Hippies went.

Goa is a small area on the west coast of India about 250 miles south of Bombay. What makes this area so unique is that besides being settled by Aryans some 2,500 years ago, it was conquered by Buddhists, Hindus, Moslems, and finally by the Portuguese in 1510 A.D.

The Portuguese were ejected in 1961, but they left their indelible mark on the culture and lifestyle of Goa. The Portuguese used Goa as a rich trading centre for spices, jewels, and riches of the east as well as a base to spread Christianity. So what is left is an area studded by churches, Portuguese style architecture, and a certain westernized Indian influence. However, the thing that attracted us most was the 60 miles of palm fringed sandy beaches. The most difficult decision to make when traveling to Goa is to decide which beach area to visit -Colva, Calangute, Baga, Anjuna, or Chapora.

Travelers whom we met told us endless stories of the beautiful beaches, friendly natives, and incredibly cheap prices. There was a constant travelers' community hanging out all through Goa. People would rent a room in a native's house right on the beach, for a few dollars a day including food.

The only inconvenience was when you visited the squatters' toilet out in the back yard. You had to take a stick with you to beat off the pigs, who would apparently scramble over to where you were squatting to get the first morsels of faeces that fell from you to the ground. The stories that our traveling friends told us were so outrageously funny that we always hoped we could visit Goa and check out their validity.

Since we could only stay in Goa for three days, we knew we wouldn't have time to search out a community of westerners to live with. So we stayed at one of the fancier hotels called the Taj Holiday Village at Fort Aguada. The most appealing attraction for me was the free bus trip from the airport to the hotel and back. I was tired of hassling my way out of airports and into cities by then. Besides the free bus trip, the resort was situated on a huge secluded palm treed property. There were clusters of rustic cottages, some one or two bedroom villas, and some suites with living rooms, each with a beautiful porch facing out toward the ocean.

As soon as the bus left the airport and started traveling through the rural areas filled with coconut trees, bullocks pulling old wooden carts and endless beaches, I felt at home. If there is such a thing as reincarnation, then I know I have lived many lifetimes in the Far East near the ocean. Some people feel at home in big cities or up in the mountains. I have felt my best lying on a beach in Bali, Sri Lanka, and Goa.

UNEASY RIDER

It's just too dangerous to ride a motorcycle in a big city. But for anyone who has a little "easy rider" in their blood, places like Nepal, Phuket and Goa are ideal. If you tour around in a car or bus, there is a barrier between you and the scenery. On a motorcycle you feel like you are part of the landscape. People would smile, children would wave, the sun shook up our sleeping melanin and we would beep the horn as we drove across the countryside. Our destination was Anjuna Beach.

From our hotel at Fort Aguada we took a local bus into Calungate. There we picked up our bargain antique motorcycle for 70 rupees per day or the equivalent of about $7.00. Along with it, just to feel safe, was a battered, black, strapless, helmet that looked like it was worn by a football player in the 1940's. Bonnie went to the State Bank of India to change money and then to MGM Travel Agency to buy a ticket out of

Goa to Bombay. I practised driving up and down the asphalt road, past the Kashmiri handicrafts, turning slowly around at the beach. Merchants called out "come see, take a look", youths laughed and asked why I rented an antique bike rather than a new one. I am sure the policeman at the beach wondered why this burnt tourist was riding up and down the same street over and over again.

I was trying to remember how to shift gears with my left foot and left hand, while putting on the brake with my right foot and giving it gas with my right hand. By the time Bonnie completed all our business, I felt like the motorcycle and I were one.

We travelled north to Baga and were enthralled with the old fishing boats lining the endless beach, topless tourists golden-brown lying on the red sand, small tourist homes, bars and restaurants, the end of the road leading to a huge mountain ridge lined in old fort ramparts.

We parked our motorcycle in the sand and ran to the water. Pulling off our clothes, we raced into the warm, clear, calm, blue salty ocean. After an hour's respite, we got the motorcycle going again and backtracked to Calangute and then on the road to Chapora. Chapora is a mixed bag. There is a small village with shops and restaurants, dense coconut palms, a rocky hill with a well preserved old Portuguese fort, paddy fields, and of course beaches both open and secluded.

We discovered Vagator Beach and plopped ourselves down next to two pretty topless European tourists. After diving into the perfect sea and frolicking in the water, a strange thing happened. Busloads of Indian tourists, fully clothed, started strolling by us on the way to the far rocks. We were told that Indian tourists liked to see the naked western travelers and actually frequented the beaches to get a glimpse of naked bodies. While I found this hard to believe, after a while the beach became quite busy. We put on our clothes and decided to continue on our way.

AJUNA MARKET

We had heard that Anjuna Beach Market on Wednesday was a big happening and that tourists and natives from all over Goa travelled especially to attend. We were surprised that there was no major roadway to get there. We had to travel along several small paths, through dry red earth fields asking everyone in sight the way to Anjuna Market. As we approached the beach we were flabbergasted. There were hundreds and hundreds of motorcycles parked at the entrance and an endless stream of people - hippies, respectable foreign tourists, and even Indian tourists from all parts of the country.

The market had a colourful, festive and friendly atmosphere. Have you ever wondered what happened to those skimpily dressed, bearded, hippies who you saw hanging around Trafalgar Square or Central Amsterdam in the 1960's? Well, they're alive and well living at the Anjuna Market. Spread over a large, flat area, interspersed among tall palm trees, about 100 yards from the ocean, was row on row of things for sale.

You could find Buddhas from Nepal, wooden boxes from India, jewellery from Tibet, leather from Italy, T-shirts, jeans, silks, hand-painted cloth and even the kitchen sink. Besides the Indian merchants who brought their crafts from all over India to sell to the tourists, many travelers made their living by bringing goods from far-off places and selling them there. Some westerners were hawking their watches, cameras, tape machines and clothes in order to pay for a ticket home.

I sat at an open-air restaurant that was playing Beatles, Rolling Stones and Joni Mitchell tapes. Beside me was an Italian man wearing short shorts, a black vest and a red bandanna. He managed quality control at a shoe factory in Bombay. Every month or so, he came to Goa to get away from the big city. Across the table, sat a young half-naked German couple and a 25 year old smiling Greek traveler who had been on the road' for two years.

This market looked like the U.N., because every conceivable nationality, race and way of dress was represented. Much to my surprise, little blue-eyed, blond haired, well-tanned children dressed in colourful Indian clothes sat among the stalls. There were many children of racially mixed marriages and some who were born in India and had never gone back to their parent's country of origin.

Although there were long lines and mobs of people, there was no pushing, rushing or hassling. Bargaining was friendly and low-keyed. I was reminded of the rock festivals of my peace-nic days. Indian merchants were calling out "change money, money change? you how much? what is your good name? just look!" We bought a small inlaid Indian jewellery box, a hand painted silk wall hanging and three hand-made black silk vests, then spent a few hours lying on the beach.

We never wanted to leave, but as the day wore on we tore ourselves away, searched and eventually found our trusty motorcycle and made our way back to the main road. Our sputtering Rajhoot motorcycle came to a halt and I couldn't get it going. Our distress didn't last long. Along came an Indian gentleman on a motorcycle, who examined our piece of junk and found that the spark plug was dead. Without any further ado he pulled out his spare and replaced our defective one.

Unwilling to accept payment, he shook our hands, smiled and rode off into the sunset.

We continued past oxen, cows, rice paddies, coconut and mango groves, huddled together mud brick brown thatched huts, while children played volleyball and soccer. Poverty was everywhere but the people were friendly, smiling and relaxed. The contrasts between this culture and our own was so dramatic that even these brief three days felt like much longer.

Goa has something for everyone. For budget conscious travelers there are small-pension like hotels, cheap restaurants and even houses or rooms in homes for rent. For the more luxury-oriented tourist, there are large resorts like the Fort Aguada Beach Resort, the Oberoi Bogmalo Beach and the Cidada de Goa where you can have all the comforts of home.

The tourist season is from November to April. The monsoons are from mid May to mid September which makes staying in Goa impossible. Most people fly to Bombay, then take the 50 minutes Indian Airlines flight to Goa. If you want luxury accommodation, then be sure to book in advance. But, if you are arriving without a reservation, then ask at the airport tourist booth or the tourist office in the capital Panaji. Or you can just set out by bus or taxi asking along the way for rooms or hotels.

GO TO GOA, before the beauty, charm, and undeveloped splendour becomes transformed by massive tourist development. Getting there is costly, but once there, you can live quite cheaply and exotically.

KASHMIR NORTHERN INDIA-LIVING LIKE A RAJ

Boy, is it hot in Delhi in July. We took our three boys on a city bus tour of temples, monuments, forts and famous sites. All they could think about was when are we going swimming? My three sons were so hot that they wanted to stay in our air conditioned room at the Janpath Hotel counting cockroaches, rather than venture outside in the furnace-like surroundings of the big city. So it was with tremendous relief that we boarded an Indian Airlines plane to fly about one hour north to Srinagar, the capital of the state of Kashmir, which is a valley nestled in the towering Himalayas on the southern periphery of Central Asia.

We weren't the first to escape the heat of Delhi to go to Kashmir. During the English rule of India, Srinagar was a hill station where the British would go to get away from the sweltering heat of the summer. Since the British couldn't own land in Kashmir, they built huge houseboats made of wood and parked them on Dal and Nageen Lakes. When the British left, the Kashmiris carried on running the boats in a style to which the English had become accustomed.

We discovered Houseboat Potamac, on Nageen Lake in 1975 and stayed ten glorious days. We felt so pampered then because our every need and whim was taken care of. In 1981, we got smarter and stayed three weeks. The family that managed the houseboat, still felt like long lost relatives and it was a tremendous feeling to be back "home". We therefore felt a little bit of trepidation in 1989 when we landed in the airport wondering if things had changed, especially after hearing stories of terrorists and political unrest.

218

Fortunately, our Kashmiri family and our boat had not seemed to be affected. Most of the Western and Indian tourists come to stay on the boats which are by and large run as family businesses. Our huge pine boat which was typical of most, had a front porch carved in cedar, which overlooked the lake and surrounding Himalayas, a living room with an intricately carved wooden ceiling, chesterfields covered in locally-designed fabric, and colourful hand knotted Kashmiri carpets on the floor.

The dining room had a dark brown walnut table with six hand carved walnut chairs, as well as a fridge where we kept our bottled water and apple juice. A small pantry served as the area where the family brought the food to be warmed before serving. There were also two bedrooms, each with two beds, plus adjoining private washrooms, with bathtub and shower.

We lived like royalty. We were served three meals a day, either in the dining room or on the top deck overlooking the lake. Our Kashmiri family cooked the food on an open hearth in their hut situated behind our boat, and brought it to us piping hot. Since our three children did not like spicy food, we chose to eat Western style cooking. For breakfast we would have pancakes, French toast, Kashmiri flat bread, regular toast with honey, butter and jam. We could have eggs cooked to our liking, if we were still hungry.

Our lunch and supper were always either mutton or chicken. We would have mutton soup once a day and chicken soup the next. Our favourite dishes included roast lamb, lamb chops, lamb kebab, and fried chicken. The children liked the French fries and baked potatoes. Our vegetables usually spinach, cauliflower, or kale were always overcooked to ensure the destruction of any germs. The desert was usually mangoes, bananas, melon or canned fruit.

To spoil us further, tea, coffee or hot lemon, with cookies or tiny buttered bagels, was served twice a day, in the late afternoon, and in the evening after the children went to bed. Can you imagine going to India to gain weight?

Kashmir has something for everyone. If you are the couch potato type, then you could hang out on the boat twenty-four hours a day, and everything would come to you. There were long, slim, flat, wooden, gondolas called Shikaras, which paddled past our boat every day laden with all we ever wanted in terms of food, handicrafts and services. Kashmiri men, with large flat paddles, came gliding past our porch, calling out their wares, announcing what they had to offer.

If we stopped them, they would board our boat and then begin bargaining. There were grocery boats carrying cookies, chocolate bars, fruit, apple juice, and assorted toiletries; flower boats chock full of the most colourful bouquets to adorn your place; boats laden with everything from wood carvings, jewellery, paper mache, postcards, furs and leather, to hand woven rugs.

Not only that, but we had tailors offering to make us anything under the sun, a daily cheap laundry service, as well as a barber who visited our boat and cut whatever hair I had left on my balding head for one dollar and fifty cents. He returned the following day to give me a full body, forty-five minute massage for three dollars. We were spoiled.

ROLLING ON THE RIVER

If you are more adventuresome and want to see the sights and scenery then there is lots to do. Most houseboats have a small shikara, that you can paddle yourself in order to make excursions around the lake to watch the kingfishers dropping to the water triumphantly catching fish, or local people digging up the weeds from the bottom.

Or you can hire shikaras equipped with colourful spring cushions, canopied to keep out the sun and nosey neighbours, paddled by trusty water-pipe smoking Kashmiris. They'll paddle you into town where you can go shopping and even wait to bring you back. Or they can take you to the famous Shalimar Gardens, built by the Moghuls in the 1600's. If you stay to catch the dazzling sunset you can hear the Sound and Light Show in the evening telling about the Valley's history.

We took an all day trip up the Jhelum River beneath the seven old bridges of Srinagar, getting a glimpse of the old architecture, the magnificent mosques and saw everyday life unfolding on the river as the native people go through their activities of daily living. We saw women washing their clothes by beating them with sticks; people defecating into the same river, followed a little further by others bathing and washing their teeth a few yards away; we saw naked boys swimming and frolicking together. Unfortunately the children threw stones and shouted insults at us as we paddled. We wondered if their behaviour reflected the underlying animosity that their parents had for foreigners or whether they were just children acting inappropriately. It was one disturbing experience that left us uneasy.

Another activity is a boat ride to the early morning market. You'll see boatloads of goods being bought and sold, and listen to the roosters cockle-doodle-doing, cows mooing and ducks quacking as you glide by. The natural scenery including magnificent water lilies, kingfishers, eagles, hawks, maple trees and reflected mountains are enchantingly peaceful and harmonious. The lake is forever changing its texture and hue.

If you want to get still more adventurous, then go on a water trek. We hired four paddlers, two boats, and a guide Farooq from our houseboat family and spent three days traveling up the Jhelum River to Manasbal Lake. They paddled up the river stopping for meals, camped in tents and built fires at night to sit around sing songs and watch the stars unfold. They carried live chickens, vegetables, and water with us in the boat, and bought meat and other food along the way.

The paddlers and Farooq waited on our every need, so there was no hardship at all. Have you ever waterskied behind a canoe? Well, my children did the next best thing. They hung on to the back of the boat while the oarsmen paddled furiously pulling them through the water. Needless to say the kids loved it.

But leave the water for a moment. What about the Himalayas? Most people go to Kashmir for the trekking. Since no one in our family wants to climb mountains "because they are there", we went hiking or should I say riding up the mountains.

The farther away from Srinagar you travel, the more isolated and untouched the places become. You come across the Gujars, a nomadic people who are sheep and goat herders. They look like people right out of the bible, dressed in long robe-like clothes, with long beards dyed in orange, carrying staffs and herding their flocks across plains and through towns.

MEADOWS OF GOLD

We drove 83 km. to Sonamarg `Meadow of Gold' through rice fields, apple orchards, past rocky streams, overshadowed by the snow-capped imposing mountains. We ate our packed lunch from home beside a fast flowing river, then rented bony ponies for a few dollars from eager horsemen. The whole family rode up the mountain for about an hour and a half to Thajiwas, a small valley at the foot of the Sonamarg Glacier, 2740 metres in height.

On another day trip we went 52 km. to Gulmarg `Meadow of Flowers'. The valley about three square miles in area, housed one of the highest golf courses in the world and was the home of skiing in the wintertime. While everyone again rented horses, I decided I would walk the twelve km. hike to the glacier and back. I did the walk fifteen years previously when I felt I couldn't afford the extra expense of horses.

This time I did it just to enjoy every nook and cranny. Bluebells, daisies, buttercups, and thistles covered the hills. I climbed over streams, chased sheep, stopped to take photos and finally exhausted from trying to keep up to the horses, arrived at the glacier at Kilanmarg. We got into an enthusiastic snowball fight, then climbed halfway up the glacier, in order to take a sleigh down. The children yelled and giggled, as they sped down the bumpy, roller-coaster-like, icy glacier, steered by a Kashmiri.

We were fortunate to spend five days in Phalgam, an idyllic mountain town, by a thunderous rushing river. We visited Wular Lake, the largest in India, as well as Achar Lake, only five km. from Srinagar and took many day trips out from our houseboat, visiting untouched villages and tourist sights. Many

people travel to Ladakh, a remote Tibetan Buddhist region north of the Himalayas, bordering on Tibet to really get away from it all. Needless to say, we had fun. But perhaps one of the most memorable experiences was the Id Festival.

KASHMIR AND THE ID FESTIVAL

Buddhism began in the Kashmir Valley, around 250 B.C. and was replaced by Hinduism around the 7th century. The conversion to Islam began in the 12th century and since the Moghuls invaded in the 16th century, the Moslem religion has a strong influence on the country's direction.

We were extremely lucky to be included in the Id-ul-Zuhara, a Moslem Festival that commemorates Abraham's attempt to sacrifice his son Ishmael to God. As you may remember from the Old Testament, Abraham and Sarah waited many years to have a son. When Isaac was born, Sarah was in her nineties, so Isaac was a very precious child to Abraham. God wanted to test Abraham's faith and asked Abraham to take his son Isaac to the top of Mount Moriah and finally sacrifice him there to God. God, seeing Abraham's willingness to sacrifice his precious son, provided a ram instead and Isaac was saved. This gesture of faith symbolized Abraham's commitment to one God and a covenant was made with the Jewish people that were to be Abraham's offspring.

Interestingly, Moslems celebrate this event and story with the Id festival. But instead of Isaac being the one sacrificed, Ishmael is the son who was chosen and taken to the temple mount by Ibrahim.

This festival is a two-day celebration. All stores are closed, people parade in the streets and firecrackers are set off. In the

225

morning all Moslems go to the mosque to pray. Everyone gets dressed in new clothes. For days before, everything in the household is washed and cleaned. It is like starting over, a combination of spring-cleaning and thanksgiving. After the visit to the mosque, the Kashmiris celebrate by slaughtering a ram or sheep. Every Moslem family in Kashmir kills an animal right there in their yards and some wealthy families will sacrifice more than one.

A few days before the slaughter was going to take place, Ali Major our houseboat owner, bought two lambs and let them graze, nibbling on the grass, next to our houseboat. My sons got to know the lambs and would go visit with them admiring their fur and talking to them. My children treated them like pets.

THE SACRIFICE

During the ceremony, a butcher came with a large knife and with the head of the household, laid the lamb down on its side and proceeded to slice it's neck while saying a prayer commemorating Ibrahim's experience.

Tears streamed down seven year old David's eyes, when he saw the lamb's neck cut and the blood coming out. It was terribly sad for him to see the animal he had made friends with, killed right before his eyes.

All the tourists watching squirmed and hid their eyes, while the Kashmiri children watched patiently without any show of emotion. It demonstrated how out of touch we have become with the killing of the food that we eat.

The Kashmiris tried to console my sobbing son telling him to stop crying. They tried to explain how lucky the sheep were to be chosen for this holy festival. They described how these animals died in a holy way, with a special prayer and ceremony, and how the food would be distributed to poor people all over. It was customary for everyone to deliver meat from the sacrifice to all their relatives, friends and the poor. No family in Kashmir supposedly went without food during this time. They also told my son how lucky it was that the sheep was slaughtered instead of Ibrahim's son.

Larry, eleven at the time, said that it is better to be familiar with the killing of our own food. He thought that he appreciated more what was involved and he had to face the truth about what we ate. It was somewhat more difficult for all of us to eat dinner that night knowing that we were eating the animals that were slaughtered right before our eyes. This was a far cry from going to the supermarket and buying meat all neatly packed in cellophane. As I mentioned previously in the chapter about the slaughter in Sulawesi, perhaps if we each personally had to kill everything we ate, then the consumption of meat might be reduced.

In Kashmir there is something special in every season. Our friends loved the spring because the valley comes alive with the blossoms of fruit trees and flowers; we loved the summer because although hot, it is not unbearable like the rest of India; the autumn with the amazing red, orange and yellow leaves falling is supposed to be spectacular; and if you love to ski, then Gulmarg offers an amazingly inexpensive ski resort.

POLITICS GETTING IN THE WAY

But like everywhere in the world, Kashmir was changing too. The forests were being ravaged, the lakes polluted, untouched

227

places were being built up, and the political climate was tense.

Kashmir had a population of over four million people and about half a million lived in Srinagar, the capital. About 90% of the population were Muslim and most were of the Sunni sect. When India and Pakistan were partitioned after independence from Britain in 1947, there was a battle over who should get Kashmir. A substantial part of Kashmir was taken over by Pakistan, but the Vale of Kashmir was under Indian control.

The long-standing issue has been whether Kashmir should remain in India or join Moslem predominant Pakistan. One group felt they were getting a raw deal from India and wanted Kashmir to become a totally independent state.

Furthermore, there was talk that Kashmiri men were going to Pakistan to be trained as terrorists, to agitate within Kashmir and prepare for the revolution that would create a Moslem type regime. India had a huge army occupying the outskirts of Srinagar and the borders with Pakistan and China. It had a force called the Border Security Police.

During our three-week stay, there had been a couple of bombings, a few Security Police killed and a number of terrorists shot. There were also general disturbances like curfews in the old city and a general strike of the merchants in protest of the treatment by the Indian Police.

In Ladakh, the Tibetan-like region bordering on China, there were conflicts between the Ledakhis and the Kashmiri merchants. The area was sealed off from travel for a few days. It seemed like the conflicts in the area were escalating and many people were disgruntled.

Although our family never felt in any danger and the disturbances were far from the houseboat area, it still left us with an unsettled feeling. This, coupled with the rise in religious fanaticism, reminded me of the feeling I had in Iran in 1975 and Sri Lanka in 1981. The turmoil has affected the tourist industry. Since tourism touches most Kashmiris, their lifestyle has suffered.

We correspond each year with our Kashmiri friends. Politics make it dangerous for us to return. Ali Major and his wonderful family are innocent bystanders in a political struggle that has transformed their life. For us, it is another place we hope will be someday restored to peace enabling us to once again visit.

CHAPTER EIGHTEEN
AFGHANISTAN, I'LL BE BACK AGAIN

Another place we will unlikely visit again for a long time is shocking Afghanistan. We heard stories about how dangerous, backward and primitive it was, so our intention during our visit in 1975, was to stay only two days. This would give us enough time to have a superficial look around and maybe hide out in our hotel if we had to.

We ended up staying two long weeks. We were surprised to find the people so friendly. Kabul, the capital, was a pleasant city with a smattering of cars, stores loaded with tourist items and restaurants serving inexpensive food. There was the occasional horseman with guns, and people dressed in costumes out of biblical times. All prices were ridiculously cheap. We "went to town", buying shirts, leather gloves, sheep skin coats, an old drum, elaborate vests, and other little treasures. We ate excellent shish kebab, the finest hot apple pie with ice cream, homemade yoghurt and rice. Every moment was an adventure.

After about five days exploring Kabul, we felt safe and relaxed. We decided to take a ride on a minibus for eight hours to Bamyan to experience the countryside. In the minibus we were huddled together, surrounded by native men on all sides, with a thermos of clean water at our feet. We travelled through desert roads, stopping occasionally at mountain villages, getting out to urinate in hole-in-the ground urinals. We finally turned a long winding corner and suddenly out of the desert loomed a lush green oasis surrounded by the Kohi Baba Mountains on one side and the Hindu Kush on the other.

In Bamyan, Buddhist monks had once lived in thousands of small caves carved out of the mountains. Two magnificent

230

standing Buddhas, one 60 feet and the other 120 feet high, were also carved right out of the rock. We climbed up to the top of the Buddha's head and overlooked the valley gazing at the snow-capped mountains in the distance.

We visited the "City of Silence", a large town built on a hill which was totally levelled by Genghis Khan. He and his armies killed every living creature in the valley. It seemed he was angry because his grandson was killed in one of the battles here, so he retaliated by reducing everything to rubble. Buddhism was annihilated and the Muslim religion took over.

A teenage boy invited us to his home for supper. We sat on the floor and ate spinach, rice and yoghurt. I played chess against him and barely won. I felt like I was playing on behalf of all of Canada, and our reputation depended on my victory.

After a few days we ventured in the back of a large open truck to Bandiamir with about 15 other travelers and locals. After three and a half hours through the desert, we came to five huge glacier lakes, each a different colour blue. The whole countryside was covered in endless wild flowers and surrounded on all sides by the Hindu Kush snow capped mountain range. There was a tiny village where travelers could stay. We stayed at the Hotel Paris in a yurt. A yurt is like an igloo made of straw. Lying in bed at night we could see through the cracks in the woven straw at the expansive sky filled with endless stars. We went exploring through the glacial lakes, wandered down into the valleys, walking ankle high in crystal clear cold water.

While exploring one exquisite lake, an Afghani man dressed in his robes, with a musket at his side, rode up on an Arabian white horse. He seemed to appear out of nowhere, and came up to where we were sitting. The horse reared back on its hind

JUST FOR THE HEALTH OF IT

legs and laughed twice. We felt like we were in an old western movie. The strange man said hello and then rode off just as quickly as he appeared.

The people of this country were simple, not politically minded, fiercely proud and independent. In 1975 when we visited, they were neutral. Both the Americans and Russians had about equal presence.

Then came the Russian Invasion transporting the country into a blood bath. Innocent people were slaughtered; remote villages without any care or knowledge about Russia or communism were reduced to rubble. The well-educated doctors, lawyers and professionals fled to India, Iran, Europe and North America. Millions died.

It was too close to Russia and within its sphere for Western countries to come to its aid. It had no strategic importance, no wealthy oil fields to make it an important place to defend. No one seemed to care. Refugee camps were set up in Iran, Pakistan and India. Tourism was destroyed.

Since the Russians left, there had been tribal warfare and military rule. The entire infrastructure of the country had been destroyed. The people lived in constant fear and danger. It is another place like Sri Lanka, Kashmir, and Iran where once tourists flocked, now few dare to go. People have suffered, refugees abound and a peaceful way of life has been altered.

Afghanistan, I'll be back again. But like Kashmir, just when, I'm not even able to guess.

CHAPTER EIGHTEEN
CHINA – BEIJING, SUZHOU, HANGZHOU

BEIJING

Have you ever felt like a speck of sand on the beach or a star in the sky? Well, go out into the streets of Beijing and join ten million people on their way to work and you will get a perspective on your insignificance on this planet.

The most sensible thing that the leaders of this city have done is to outlaw motorcycles. Bicycles are quite enough. Millions of bicycles wind their way through the streets, weaving and merging, relaxed and yet unyielding. The occasional ringing of bells to warn pedestrians, the odd calling out to let people know they are coming but generally expressionless, easy going riders on their way to work. During our visit in 1995 we did not see any ten speeds, or fancy colours, or lightweight models, just a sea of mostly black bikes creaking along.

Here was a city being constructed overnight. Cranes, scaffolding, huge edifices taking up massive spaces, are dotted everywhere. Sixty per cent of the people of this city lived in one or two room apartments with no running water or toilets. These facilities were shared often in a courtyard adjoining many homes. Modern high-rises contrast the squalor of tiny alleyways.

Sightseeing starts everywhere. Just stop on any corner and the fun begins. You don't have to seek out the temples, palaces, museums, or parks to see the sights. Just stand around and gawk and be gawked at. There are few policemen, no gas stations, no cats, dogs or birds, but just cars, bikes and lots and

235

lots of people. Everything seems casual and friendly, with no screaming, hurrying, or pushing except when you try to get on the buses or subway and then it's everyone for themselves.

You have to sharpen your elbows. There is no such thing as a line-up but instead there is "bunching". You gather around and push your way to the front. I was the first one off the airplane bus getting ready to board the plane. I still can't understand how everyone on the whole bus pushed and weeded their way in front of me.

Touring always gets down to the basics of time and money. If time is not an issue, then touring by foot, bus, subway and taxi on your own are less expensive and you have more freedom to stop and stare, be spontaneous and meet people. All you really need is a good map, a guidebook, good walking shoes, pen and paper. Since most people don't speak English be sure to have someone at your hotel write down in Chinese lettering the names of your destinations so you can show it to people when you get lost. But if time is short, then you can go to any number of tourist offices and join a group with a guide.

THE GREAT WALL

Don't leave China without a visit to the Great Wall. An inexpensive and not so well known way to go is by train. Go to the Beijing Railway Station and step up to the International or Foreign Passengers Room and reserve an express soft seat air-conditioned train the night before you go.

As you leave built-up Beijing toward the countryside, you pass factories, housing developments, farms, and gently rolling hills, until you finally get off at the train station 1 km. from The Wall.

The Wall has always fascinated me. When the astronauts were out in space and looked at our tiny world the only man-made structure they could see was the Great Wall. I 've seen it on TV and in photos but nothing prepared me for this huge, massive structure which goes on and on for some 5,000 km. across the whole of China. Can you just imagine the Emperor Qin some 2,000 years ago deciding that a wall would be a good idea to keep out the wild nomads from the north? Then in the middle of nowhere, across mountains and valleys through every kind of terrain, this Wall was constructed. The number of lives lost and the extent of human suffering for this construction must have been colossal.

We spent a few hours climbing the steep, uneven stairs of this imposing edifice and then kept going on the completely deserted unrestored part. We walked about 3 km. over parts that were crumbling, and grown over with grass and shrubs. We had a picnic of hard-boiled eggs, croissants and water. It was so peaceful.

I felt a sense of majesty, high up in the mountains, the wind blowing, silence all around standing on top of this enormous man-made structure. There is nothing in the world to compare it with. As wonderful as you may expect the Wall to be, it really is better.

Remember to arrange for a taxi to take you back to the train and be sure to buy a ticket for the train ride back to Beijing before you leave the station. We didn't because we just assumed there would be a way back to the station. Much to our surprise, there were no taxis to take us back, so we walked around the parking lot approaching different tour buses to see if any would take pity on us and give us a ride to Beijing.

Late in the afternoon, we ended up hitching a ride with a

Chinese tour bus and spent quite some time haggling with the non-English speaking bus driver and tour guide about how much we would pay. A number of times they threatened to kick us off the bus when we told them their exorbitant price was too much. Even after we agreed to a price, they continued to rudely shout at us and make fun of us, in Chinese, in front of the whole bus. We ended up sitting in the folded-down, ragged, uneven, bumpy seats in the middle of the aisle all the way to Beijing. We were thankful we had a ride back and tolerated the loss of face and the verbal abuse without much complaining. We arrived back embarassed but safe.

SPITTING

We were quite hot when we finally made it back to our hotel. I couldn't wait to jump into the hotel's swimming pool. Spitting is common on Beijing streets and I did hear and see the art of spitting being practised proficiently. But I never expected what I was about to experience.

My children and I dressed quickly in our swimsuits and walked to the pool. Just as I was about to get in, one of the gentlemen began spitting loudly at the stairway to the pool, making horrible horking sounds into the water. I was hot, and really wanted to get in. I decided to go to the opposite end of the pool away from the spitter. As I strolled to the other side, an older woman began blowing her nose with her hand into that side. If that wasn't enough, another man started spitting into the water as well.

When I say spitting I don't mean just a little bit. I mean repugnant noises coming from the bottom of the guy's guts. I thought he was going to spit out his intestines. He just didn't do it once by mistake; he spit over and over again almost like a ritual. Needless to say, my appetite for swimming quickly vanished and I decided to go to my room and shower instead.

TIANANMEN SQUARE

Another must for Beijing is Tiananmen Square. Most of us would never have heard of this huge gathering space if it hadn't been for the massacre of hundreds of student demonstrators for democracy in 1989. This is the largest public square in the world and there are many buildings and monuments to visit. You can easily spend a day visiting all the sights. You can't help but notice a large red structure at the north end of the Square with a gigantic photo of Mao Zedong reminding you of his influence as the founder of modern China. It was here, at Tienanmen Gate (Gate of Heavenly Peace) that Mao proclaimed the People's Republic of China in 1949. You walk through this gate to the Forbidden City.

Also on Tienanmen Square is the Qianmen (Front Gate), which used to guard the wall separating the ancient inner city and the outer area built in the 15th century; Monument to the People's Heroes, an obelisk with carvings of revolutionary events; The Great Hall of the People, where the National People's Congress sits and of course the Mausoleum, which houses the body of Chairman Mao. There is certainly no leader in modern history that has had as profound an effect on China as Mao.

THE FORBIDDEN CITY

The Forbidden City is the palace that was built between 1406-1420 by Emperor Yong Le and occupies some 720,000 square metres, 800 buildings and some 900 rooms. In other words, this place is big. It takes about a half day to walk through it.

The emperors really knew how to have a good time. They constructed this huge city where they lived completely isolated from the rest of the population. It was forbidden to anyone except the royal family, their concubines, soldiers, ministers and servants. You walk through huge gates to three halls where the emperor received his guests. These ornate structures, flanked by immense courtyards, were given names that tell you their primary focus.

The Hall of Supreme Harmony is the largest structure and was used for ceremonial occasions. The Hall of Middle Harmony, the Hall of Preserving Harmony, Palace of Heavenly Purity , and the different palaces where the royalty lived are each worth a careful visit. There are beautiful stone carvings, intricate roofs, painted ceilings, bronze statues of lions, cranes, and other animals. I got the impression that being one of the 24 emperors who lived here in succession during the Ming and Qing Dynasties would have been a pleasurable experience. David who was twelve years old, decided after seeing the palace, that when he grows up he wants to become an emperor.

If the weather was too hot in the summer, then the emperor had the Summer Palace about 12 kilometres away in the suburbs of Beijing and a must for you as a tourist to see. The Empress Dowager Cixi rebuilt this immense park to her liking in 1888 and created quite a retreat. There are a number of beautiful temples, gardens and the famous Long Corridor decorated with mythical scenes spanning some 700 metres. You can take a boat ride across a large man-made lake, pass a 17 arch marble bridge and visit the South Lake Island. You need a half a day to visit this royal playground.

If you've gone to the Great Wall, visited Tienamen Square, the Forbidden City and the Summer Palace then you still have a choice of parks, temples and museums which deserve your attention. My favourite temples are the Tiantan (Temple of Heaven) and the Lama Temple. There are also the Museum of the Revolution, Natural History Museum, and a Museum of Traditional Chinese Medicine and Acupuncture that are worthwhile.

The best time to visit the parks is early in the morning between 6:00 and 8:00 a.m. when thousands of residents head for the parks taking their song birds for some fresh air and a walk. They hang their ornate cages on trees while they go about doing T'ai Chi, meditation, ballroom dancing, or aerobics to disco music from ghetto blasters. Each group is assembled scattered amongst the trees, water fountains and paths. There were a surprising number of older people congregated together doing exercise. Not only does this provide an early morning communal spirit but gets people going, before they go to work. Don't miss the Beihai, Tiantan and Ritan Parks.

One of our favourite activities was meandering through the Hutongs or small lanes in the older sections of the city. You can see the little shops and people carrying out their lives down narrow alleyways. Go out walking along the side roads in the morning when everyone is on their way to work. See people dressed in neat suits and good-looking clothes emerge from a dingy hovel. I wondered how they coped living in seeming squalor and yet working in offices and shops during the day. Smells, people sleeping on the streets, morning markets, neighbourhood restaurants, and barbers cutting hair on the street were memories I will cherish.

If you are really brave and somewhat crazy, then rent a bike and see how you manage with the lawlessness of the roads. Cars and bikes occasionally stop at red lights if someone stops in front of them, but the practice of making right and left turns through red lights without stopping left me speechless and frightened. Might gets the right of way, so if you are driving a big vehicle you always win. Pedestrians clearly have no rights and it is just one big game of chicken.

Buses are cheap, but as I mentioned earlier, it helps to get the destinations written down ahead of time so you can show the person taking tickets where you want to go. There are a number of grades of taxis depending on their size, with each size costing a different fare. We always chose the cheapest taxi. Don't expect drivers to speak English. Taxis are cheap enough that if you went everywhere you wanted to go by taxi you would still pay less then if you went on an organized tour, especially if you have more than one person with you.

If you don't want to feel left out, get a good guidebook on China and join the rest of the throngs of tourists carrying one. Visit the Great Wall, Tiananmen Square, Forbidden City, The Summer Palace, a few temples and parks and you will have unforgettable memories.

SUZHOU-CHINA'S VENICE OF THE EAST

Visiting cities like Beijing and Shanghai can be a little overwhelming because of their size. That's why visiting Suzhou which is more rural, undeveloped and approachable than either Beijing or Shanghai is a good idea.

Imagine a city founded in 514 BC and reaching its peak around 1000 years ago. Located in the province of Jiangsu and situated on the Grand Canal and the Changjiang River, it was so strategically located it became a centre for shipping and grain storage. By the 14th century Suzhou was the leading silk producer in the country and presently it produces 30% of all the silk in China.

We orientated ourselves by taking a boat ride down the Grand Canal looking at life on the water. The Grand Canal, the world's longest artificial canal, stretches from Hangzhou to Beijing some 1800 km and was built 2400 years ago. It was finally linked together in the 7th century, and is still a transportation route. You could take a journey from Suzhou to Wuxi or even Hangzhou to get a real taste of the extent of this ancient waterway.

The boat ride reminded me of Venice, Italy and Srinagar, Kashmir in Northern India which is also referred to as the "Venice of the East". We saw people living on houseboats, carrying on their daily activities of eating, washing, shopping, and cleaning. Small boats and huge barges passed by carrying all kinds of cargo from vegetables to building materials like sand, straw and bricks. Unlike Srinagar where the children were abusive, calling us names and throwing stones, the people on the boats were smiling and friendly, often waving as we passed. There were many smaller canals and numerous beautiful stone bridges to sit on and watch life float past.

GARDEN CITY

Besides being called the Venice of the East, Suzhou is also called the Garden City. Unique among its numerous historical and scenic spots inside and outside the town are the finest specimens of classical gardens built during the Song, Yuan, Ming and Qing Dynasties. It is the famous gardens that draw many horticulturists from around the world. Unlike the massive imperial gardens in other cities, these were originally designed and created by private merchants, artisans and scholars.

The beauty is created by a mixing together of rocks, water, trees, flowers and buildings. The purpose was to create a peaceful, enchanting place to retreat. It's difficult to appreciate this if you are part of a tour where a certain time is allotted and you have to clamour over hundreds of people to get a view.

The gardens are best appreciated if you can leisurely stroll through and stop at your favourite spot and sit for at least fifteen minutes contemplating the creator's design. There are many gardens to choose from, each with interesting names. There is the Humble Administrator's Garden, Lion Grove, Blue Wave Pavilion, Garden of Harmony and the Garden for Lingering In.

Our guide chose the Garden of the Master of the Nets because it was smaller and she used to go there when she was a student. Instead of studying, she used to sit with a book in front of her and "space out", lost in the tranquil atmosphere. I liked the way the garden mixed with the buildings to compliment the structures.

The designer, in the 12th century during the Song Dynasty, combined unusually shaped rocks, ponds and trees to give a sense of serenity and peace. Green pointed roofs, goldfish swimming, Ming style furniture and lanterns all complimented and contradicted each other. The whole idea of a "picture window" rings true when you visit each room. From every window there is a well-thought-out view designed like a beautiful picture. It made me want to go home and look out each of my windows in my house and create better scenes.

SILK FACTORIES

No visit to Suzhou would be complete without visiting a silk factory. I'm sure you all know silk comes from worms and although in the past I had heard something about how the process was done, it wasn't until this visit that I truly fathomed just how incredible the production of silk really is. It all starts with a moth, which lays about 400 eggs. The eggs hatch into worms and the best of the worms are chosen. The worms are attached to mulberry bushes and after chewing away for about 25 days the worm grows to its full size. The worm spits out silk to make its cocoon and this process of spinning its cocoon takes about two days.

Here is where the fun starts. The cocoons are gathered from the mulberry bushes and taken to the factory. Here row on row of women sit operating machines. During the first stage, the cocoons are put in boiling water, thus killing the larva inside. A special machine finds the filament at the end of the cocoon and unravels the whole thing. The machine then joins it with 10 to 11 other filaments to make a thread. The quality and grade of silk is determined by how many filaments go into the silk thread that is used. Poor quality silk might use only six filaments to make its thread.

It takes about 900 to 1000 cocoons to make a silk shirt! The chrysalides are discarded and are used to make medicine and oils. Very high in protein, apparently one chrysalid is equivalent to six eggs. The raw silk is washed and dried and then put onto spools ready for export or making silk garments and articles. Next time you put on a silk shirt or underwear, appreciate what goes into its production.

If you enjoy markets, then don't miss the special night market. Clothes and household items were being sold to the locals. The streets were closed to traffic and you could stroll along mixing with the native shoppers. The Chinese were still extremely curious about foreigners and the novelty of seeing us had not worn off in small towns. So if you would really like to gather a crowd, then stop at one of the stands and try something on.

Soon groups of curious onlookers will surround you and you will become the main attraction. Bonnie tried on a hat and suddenly there were at least thirty people all crowding around to get a stare at the tall, blond, longhaired Caucasian woman. It was fun and we always felt safe.

Interesting canals, beautiful gardens, special temples, silk factories and friendly people make Suzhou an enjoyable place to visit. This Silk Centre, Garden City, Venice of the East, does not have the crowded feeling of a big high-rise city and is more relaxed and easy going. Visit for two or three nights and I'm sure you'll find the place fascinating.

An old Chinese saying relates that "Above there is heaven, below there is Suzhou and Hangzhou." So after Suzhou we headed for Hangzhou.

HANGZHOU'S FOR YOU

As a child growing up in Toronto I was curious about China. My parents told me that if I dug straight down into the ground and kept on going I would reach that mysterious land. I always wanted to see who was on the opposite side of the world from Canada and discover how they walked upside down. Whenever I didn't want to finish my food, my parents tried to elicit guilt by telling me that there were people starving in China. I remember replying that I would gladly send them my leftover liver with onions, but my mother didn't seem to think that was a very good reply. As I got older, I heard that people in China were no longer starving and I wanted to go there to find out how you feed 1.2 billion people.

Since China opened to tourism in the 1980's most visitors go via organized tours across a well-beaten path. Although there are 21 provinces and five autonomous regions, the majority of tourists don't get to one of the smallest provinces Zhejiang and it's capital city Hangzhou. Founded in 221 B.C. during the Qin dynasty, this ancient city of 1.3 million, forms part of the rich Yangzi River Delta.

Since it is water accessible and has such rich fertile soil, it has been an important trading centre noted for it's famous tea and silk. Zhejiang province produces a third of China's raw silk and it's tea is supposed to be the best in China. The Grand Canal, stretches some 1800 km from Hangzhou all the way to Beijing. The best time to see this heavenly city is in April and May when the flowers are in blossom. We went at the end of June when it rained and flooded.

Hangzhou is situated on the famous West Lake, one of its main tourist attractions. The Lake is about 3 km long and over 2 km wide and was originally a lagoon adjoining the Qintang River. It was dredged in the 8th century and the earth was used to form a causeway crossing the lake. There are a number of islands to visit, the largest, Solitary Hill, houses the Provincial Museum and the Zhonshan Park.

One morning, we took a stroll through Flower Harbour Park, famous for its huge goldfish, symbols of wealth and its beautiful peonies, representing good luck. There by the shore of the West Lake we boarded an intricately carved, gold leafed trimmed, wooden Oriental boat and cruised across West Lake to the second biggest island.

Three Pools Mirroring the Moon Island is named after three poles that stick out of the water. During a special holiday festival on August 15th, the moon is reflected in the water between three poles. This island within the West Lake has three lakes within it, so 60% of the island's surface is water.

It is exquisitely planned out with beautiful flower gardens, lily ponds, a large zigzag bridge, and a huge reflecting mirror where you must take a photo of yourself taking a photo of yourself. If you have the time stroll through a path of bamboo to a garden of peace and harmony and visit the monastery in the middle. Unfortunately our tour only allowed a quick walk through so we didn't have much of a chance to get into a meditative state of mind.

PAGODA HEAVEN

Our next stop was the Six Harmonies Pagoda located to the southwest of the city overlooking the enormous rail and road bridge that crosses the Qiantang River. The huge 60 meters high, wooden octagonal pagoda is quite striking and was named for the six codes of Buddhism.

Pagodas are plentiful in China and if you wander out back of the Six Harmonies Pagoda, you will find a museum of pagodas that shows photos and tells about the history of pagodas in China. The pagoda originated from India and was built to house Buddhist relics as well as being a tomb for monks. Since they were built out of wood many were destroyed by fire, wars and recently during the Cultural Revolution. But thousands of pagodas are still standing throughout China.

There is a beautiful bonsai garden behind the museum. I was surprised to learn that bonsai originated in China and that the Japanese took this interest in bonsai gardening from them. Walk through the bonsai garden and tour the garden of pagodas. Here there is a map of China showing where all the famous pagodas are located. There are large replicas of each pagoda scattered around a huge garden. If you are not going to travel the whole of China, here is a perfect way to experience the magnitude of the pagoda sights possible. I was astonished at how many beautiful structures are still standing after so many wars and destruction.

Luckily tourism has been an encouragement for the government to preserve and restore its religious heritage. It realizes that tourists like to see old religious structures, so there has been an effort to repair these sights which were unkempt for many years. Be sure to climb to the top of the hill out back so you will be able to have the best view and photo of the large rail and road bridge across the Qiantang River.

INSPIRED SECLUSION

The Temple of Inspired Seclusion is worth a visit. Our guide advised us it was not on our itinerary and was going to take us to a silk factory, but I asked persuasively enough that he consented to take us. It was pouring rain the whole time we toured and luckily we did have an umbrella.

The Lingyin Si Temple was built by an Indian monk in 326 AD and apparently has been destroyed and rebuilt 16 times. The present buildings were last restored in the Qing Dynasty.

There are four things not to be missed.

First there is the Hall of the Four Heavenly Guardians that has a statue of Buddha in the middle flanked with two statues of protectors on each side. Two of the protectors are fierce using sword and serpent. Two statues guard Buddha using peaceful weapons, an umbrella with the Buddhist scriptures written on it and a pipa guitar.

Second there is the Great Hall which houses the 20 metre high golden sitting Buddha with many statues of high-ranking monks carved around the perimeter of the room.

Third, don't miss the garden of Buddhas. You'll find a map showing the location of the great Buddha statues in China and then a walk-through garden where you can see the most famous replicas of Buddha in his many poses. They are all carved out of concrete, with some replicas the full size of the originals.

The fourth and most fascinating thing to see is the rocky hill, Felai Feng, which had some 330 chiselled sculptures of Buddhas in hundreds of postures. You get to climb up and down the rocky hill, into caves, across a stream, and everywhere you look there are beautiful carvings. I could have spent a day just gazing at all the countenances and facial expressions of the various sculptures.

I've always wondered why there is a fat laughing Buddha image that shows up in carvings in many places of the world. In Sri Lanka, India, Thailand and Indonesia where there are Buddha handicraft carvings I saw replicas of the fat laughing Buddha but I never saw a fat laughing Buddha sculpture in any temple. I began to wonder if the image was totally an invention.

The whole image of Buddha being a fat man was incongruous with the concept of restraint. Well, here carved out of the rock hill were two fat Laughing Buddhas. Our guide said that he was fat because he was all accepting and his laughter made him more accessible to the common person. Even though life is suffering, the Buddha laughs. So when we are faced with hardship in our life we can think of the Laughing Buddha and it will make us laugh too. I always hated that Buddha image because I never imagined Buddha who had given up all attachments, desires, and possessions to be fat. After seeing the original and hearing the explanation I was more willing to accept this unBuddha-like fat man.

If you like zoos and appreciate modern, spacious, well-thought-out, respectful to animals-type zoos then stay away from the Hangzhou Zoo. It's despicable to see how the animals are kept. This is generally true of most zoos in South East Asia. I was saddened to see the pandas, bears, tigers and other animals. Worst of all was the most pitiful lion I have ever seen. I could not imagine he would live much longer.

The Yellow Dragon Cave Temple, built in the 13th century is noteworthy because it had a marvellous Teahouse. A classical Chinese orchestra consisting of flute, Chinese horn, two stringed Chinese violins, mandolin like guitar called a pipa as well as an xylophone-like harp and cymbals played Chinese melodies. The orchestra takes requests and you pay a small amount after the song is performed. Also at this temple for a price, you can dress up in emperor's clothes and take photos. The Chinese opera is usually performed on stage but the day we went there was no performance.

FIVE FOR TEA

The Hangzhou area is known for its famous Dragon Well green tea which is supposed to be number one in China. We passed fields of tea, visited a tea factory, got to partake in a tea ceremony and learned something of the tea making process. There are 16 grades of green tea and it's picked between late March and early October. After the leaves are hand picked they are hand dried in a hot iron bowl for more than an hour. Ordinarily tea is dried by machines or sunshine and this causes it to ferment. This hand-dried technique ensures its purity since no chemicals or fermentation takes place.

This tea is promoted as being high in vitamin C, A, chlorophyll, amino acids and anti-cancer substances. We were told that the Dragon Well village where the tea originates is famous for its longevity and that the average age of the elderly people is 87. They claimed that no one has died of cancer since 1970. My scientific doctor mind wanted to see the double-blind randomly controlled studies.

There are six stages to drinking this tea. First, you put the tealeaves into a glass or cup. Next you pour the hot water into a teapot and let it cool down a little. Then you half fill the cup with hot water but don't dare drink the tea. This is the time for smelling the aroma. After a good whiff, you add the rest of the water and taste. You are to drink the rest of the tea but leave a small bit in the bottom of the glass. Pour the third cup and appreciate the colour and shape of the leaves. You can eat the leaves if you wish.

Of course you must drink quite slowly and taste each cup carefully. This process does not destroy the vitamin C. Other teas like Indian and Oolong tea are half fermented and so some of the vitamin C is destroyed. Black tea is totally fermented and because it is left to stand in boiling water, all the vitamin C is destroyed. It's difficult to escape Hangzhou without buying it's famous tea for gifts back home.

If you enjoy flea markets, then stroll along the night market that is set up at the edge of West Lake. There are throngs of people, hundreds of stalls and all kinds of trinkets and souvenirs to buy. People were friendly everywhere and we never sensed danger at any time. Taking a boat ride on the West Lake at night can be a romantic and fun excursion. Either charter a boat for a cruise or rent paddleboats where you do all the work but have more freedom and privacy.

Hangzhou has beautiful gardens, special temples, the famous West Lake, teas and silk factories, night markets and interesting history. Hangzhou has something for you.

CHAPTER NINETEEN
MADE IN TAIWAN

Did you ever notice that many things you buy have "Made in Taiwan" stamped on it? How can such a small island have such a huge economic impact? It's not until you visit there yourself that you can really understand.

The population is highly educated and places education as one of its top priorities for their children. They are a hard-working, industrious people and provide a cheap labour market for their factories. Although I would find it scary to live only 160 km. off the southeast coast of mainland China, Taiwan has used its strategic location in the South China Sea to be a go-between East and West. It is this combination of the traditions of the East and modern conveniences of the West that makes it an interesting tourist destination.

The island is only 144 km. at its maximum width and 395 km. at its maximum length. Ninety per cent of the population lives on a narrow plain on the west coast, with Taipei the busy, booming capital in the north. Being one of the most densely populated areas in the world, the traffic jams, with lines of taxi cabs and thousands of motorbikes weaving in and out makes it a chore to go anywhere. It almost seems like rush hour is never ending. Although the traffic is terrific, bus service in Taipei is good and the rapid transit, subway system makes it easier to get around.

To understand Taiwan it helps to know a little about it's history. In 1517 the Portuguese came to Taiwan and named it Formosa which meant beautiful. The name was popular among foreigners for many years but is no longer used. The Dutch took control of the southwestern part in 1624 and introduced modern farming and brought many Chinese settlers from the mainland. In 1683 the Manchus took over and Taiwan became a county of mainland China until 1895 when after the Sino-Japanese War, the Japanese took control. Japan occupied the Island for the next fifty years until after their defeat in 1945.

When the communists took control of the mainland in 1949, the Kuomintang led by Chiang Kai-shek fled to Taiwan and established the government. Chiang Kai-Shek ruled Taiwan until his death in 1975. His son Chiang Chingkuo took over as President from his father until he died in 1988. His successor Lee Teng-hui came to symbolize new democratic freedoms including opposition parties, freedom of speech and human rights.

NATIONAL PALACE MUSEUM-TREASURES SAVED

When Chiang Kai-shek and the Nationals fled Mainland China in 1949, they took with them thousands of Chinese treasures. Communist China has not been happy with this and has contended that they belong to the mainland and wants them back. However during the Cultural Revolution in the 1960's, thousands of artefacts and works of art were purposefully destroyed in Mainland China. If it had not been for the relics saved in Taiwan, then many of the valuable pieces would have been lost forever.

Anyone visiting Taipei must see the National Palace Museum that has perhaps the best collection of Chinese artefacts, calligraphy, paintings and porcelain in the world. There are so many relics that there has to be a continuous changing of exhibits in order to display all the treasures. Give yourself at least three or four hours to explore the various exhibits.

Although I previously visited China, spending time reading about Chinese History and touring through the museums in Beijing, I still had difficulty understanding the history of the various dynasties and putting it all into some context. A special exhibit concerning the relationship between Chinese History and World Culture at the Palace Museum put everything into perspective.

This exhibit traced the development of China's civilization starting some 5,000 years ago and compared it to what was happening in the rest of the world. Gunpowder, printing, the compass, paper, and certain kinds of machinery were developed in China as well as advances in the field of astronomy, medicine and the arts. I finally could follow visually each succeeding period from the Yellow River Valley, the Shang, Zhou, Han, and Chou Dynasties including the spread of Confucianism, Buddhism and their influences on the rest of the world. Seeing Western Culture also displayed help me understand the time line of many inventors, scientists, and artists in the world.

A RAGING BULL IN A CHINA SHOP

I raced through exhibits of Chinese pottery, costume accessories, ritual bronze vessels, calligraphy treasures, sort of like drive by sightseeing on foot. I'm glad I wore my Nike Airs. I slowed down considerably for the exhibition of a Royal Tomb from the late Shang Dynasty some 3,300 years ago. Emphasis is placed on the great beauty and advanced craftsmanship of the various carved objects of stone and bone as well as white clay pottery, jades and bronze vessels. Photographs of the actual excavation process were included to give an impression of the vast scale of the construction of the grave mound of a Shang king.

When finally excavated, the tomb was a large pit, with the north-south leg about 69 meters long and the east west leg about 46 metres in length. Bones of at least 164 sacrificial victims were found in various parts of the tomb and at least 59 people had been decapitated. It must have been quite a funeral.

I must confess that I have never been enthralled by Chinese paintings. The symbolism, simplicity, and subject matter are often too subtle for my baby boomer mentality. Yet when I took the time to view the collection of famous paintings and followed the trends and transitions from the earliest Neolithic period to the Ming and Ch'ing dynasties, I couldn't help but marvel at the attention to fine details, the beautiful landscapes, flower and bird designs and the regard for tradition and restraint. Now I find Chinese paintings exceedingly comforting and relaxing.

The Palace Museum is located on the outskirts of the city and is easily accessible by bus or taxi depending on what you can afford. There are good conducted English tours. It would be a grave mistake to visit Taiwan and not see this museum.

CHIANG KAI-SHEK MEMORIAL

The other attraction you won't want to miss visiting is the Chiang Kai-Shek Memorial. It is an enormous building in the centre of town occupying an area of 250,000 square metres. Surrounded by a 1,200-metre walk, the grounds include magnificent ornamental red flowerbeds, tree-lined avenues and green lawns together with winding pathways, two carp lakes, three exercise areas, and rockeries. To either side of the Memorial Hall is the National Theatre and National Concert

Hall each with its lovely decorative roof.

Early in the morning, beginning at about six o'clock, you can observe people in hordes doing t'ai chi, ballroom dancing and all sorts of exercise on the grounds of the Memorial. The people love it if you join in.

The Memorial Hall itself is 70 metres high, has white marble walls and is capped by an octagonal roof done in blue glazed tiles. The Hall's upper floor houses a large bronze statue of Chiang Kai-Shek behind which stands the inscription "Ethic, Democracy, Science". There are huge bronze double doors forming an arch 16 meters high and weighing 75 tons. The Hall's ground floor contains relics, exhibition rooms, a film theatre, two art galleries, a library, an audiovisual centre and the CKS memorial office.

The memorial office depicts the first President's office exactly like it was when he was in power. The origin and significance of all the furniture and art pieces are described on a interactive TV monitor in the hall outside. There is a life-size wax model of the President sitting behind his desk. You really get a feel for what it must have been like when he was in power. The history about what was going on before and during the founding of modern China, told through the eyes of Chiang Kai Shek puts a different perspective on the politics during the 1940's.

Besides visiting the National Palace Museum and the Chiang Kai-Shek Memorial, it is pleasant to take a drive up the mountain north of Taipei to visit the National Park and Hot Springs. It is cooler and the air is fresher as you get higher. Mount Yang-min is a popular recreation area and the town of Pei-t'ou at its base has the hot springs and the Pi-t'an or Green Lake has boating and water sports.

A few other attractions that are worthwhile are the Lungshan or Dragon Mountain Temple, the Kuantu Temple and the famous Snake Alley. No visit to Taiwan would be complete without a visit to the Karaoke TV Restaurant and Bar.

Taiwan is famous for its fresh and superb food. Seafood is bountiful and we ate creatures from the deep that we had never encountered before. Fruits, though expensive, are plentiful and we delighted at being able to eat mangosteens, rambutans, mangoes and lychee fruit to our heart's content.

Food and water seem fairly safe and the medical care is of good quality. The vast focus of the medical system is westernized. The National Taiwan University Hospital I visited is comparable to most hospitals in North America.

One of the more memorable things about Taiwan is the people. The population is of Chinese descent and the official language, Mandarin, is the same as mainland China. The religion is mostly Buddhist or Taoist with a Confucian influence. Generally everyone was quite respectful, customs are upheld, shoes are taken off before entering a home and people bow slightly to show respect.

English is taught in school and although there are not many English signs like in Hong Kong, most people especially the youth, can speak English or at least write and read English superbly. On a few occasions people couldn't understand us when we spoke so we wrote what we had to say on paper and then they could understand perfectly.

So if you are passing through Taiwan and wondering if you should stop and have a look, by all means stay for a few days. The friendly people, delicious food, National Palace Museum, Chiang Kai-Shek Memorial and the temples make this a worthwhile tourist destination. Even with industrialization, terrible traffic and heavy pollution, there are many redeeming qualities that can make a visit to Taiwan rewarding.

CHAPTER TWENTY
OH CANADA – ALGONQUIN PARK

In 1957, my parents took me to Algonquin Park and I was amazed that deer came right up to the side of the road and ate out of my hand. Later as a nineteen-year-old camp counsellor I took a group of thirteen-year-old boys on a three-day canoe trip through the Park, sleeping out, and gazing at the expansive sky.

Although I was born and bred an urban suburbanite and though I'd never want to live anywhere but where the action is, there is still a longing I have to see the sky unobstructed by high buildings, to wander in fields bedazzled by wild flowers and to swim in lakes still crystal clear and unpolluted. I still shiver inside when I hear the mournful cry of a loon, see a bull moose sloshing amidst the marshes, or a frisky deer running across a back road.

Since 1978, working as a camp doctor, I've been sneaking up to Algonquin Park each summer to try and set my soul free. In the big city, skyscrapers block the sky, with a building looming on every corner. In Northern Ontario the sky is so expansive, that the Big Dipper, Milky Way, Northern Lights, shooting stars, and satellites provide hours of silent entertainment.

Algonquin Park is located on the southern edge of the Canadian Shield between the Ottawa River and Georgian Bay. It is about a three and a half hour drive north from Toronto. Most visitors to the Park travel along highway 60 and visit the eight campgrounds or thirteen walking trails in the Algonquin Parkway Corridor. Although there are nearly 7700 sq. km. of forests, lakes and rivers most of the people who visit Algonquin spend most of their time off highway 60.

261

In the mid 1800's, the white man began systematically cutting down the magnificent white and red pine that were taken by ship to Britain. By the end of the 1800's nearly all these huge trees were gone. Today when you see a few scattered three hundred year old trees, forty metres tall and 1.5 metres diameter around, you can imagine how spectacular the forest must have been.

The Park was established in 1893 to preserve what was left of the natural forest and to provide a recreational area for the people of Ontario. But even by that time, the logging industry and man-made caused fires as a result of that industry had altered the "virgin wilderness".

There is a lot offered in an organized way by the Ministry of Natural Resources. Every night there are different evening programs, about the timber wolf, the black bear, a beaver pond, wild flowers, canoe tripping and other naturalist topics. There are conducted walks exploring insects, ecology, trees, and mushrooms as well as canoe and camping demonstrations.

If you bring along children, they'll enjoy the "Algonquin for Kids" demonstrations, learning about wildlife up close through games, stories and animals. So if you are not the type who likes to get lost by yourself on some unmarked path, or take a canoe ride to an out-of-the way lake, or travel for days out into the wilderness, then Algonquin still has lots for you.

I appreciate the safety of being in Northern Ontario. Having travelled all over the world, I feel safest in Algonquin Park. I'm sure there is petty crime in Algonquin just like anywhere else, and you still have to lock your car and keep your food out on a limb so bears and raccoons can't reach it. But there is less danger there in terms of automobiles, guns, hold-ups, and drugs. There are no poisonous snakes, or poison ivy and only a few people have been killed by running their auto into a moose at night. Also if there was a nuclear war this wouldn't be a bad place to hide.

My favourite scheduled activity is the bird walks usually held on one or two mornings a week throughout the summer. Birders from all over the world gather in the Old Airfield parking lot, armed with bird books, binoculars and lots of enthusiasm. The Old Airfield is a large open field that was cleared as an emergency landing spot during World War Two. On its borders are a marsh, a lake and forests made of deciduous and conifer trees. In this way you can see birds living in three distinct habitats.

PISHING IS FUN

A park naturalist leads the thirty or so visitors for an hour and a half journey searching for birds. Everyone crowds around as Sean, the Park Naturalist explains the significance of the songs and calls of the birds. If you visit in June, the airfield is filled with many different songs. When the birds first arrive in the spring it is their job to find a mate, stake out a territory for the nest and settle down to raise a family. The song attracts a mate and warns other birds not to invade its feeding space.

As we approach a small wooded area just beside the parking lot, we all stop to listen. Our senses are heightened, all ears are open and all eyes on the skies and trees. Suddenly something darts across the sky and everyone turns in hot pursuit. It's two Merlin Hawks swooping through the air, putting on an air show. Merlin Hawks feed on small birds and are quite rare to the Park. It's the first time I've seen one and everyone including Sean is very excited.

263

All eyes and binoculars turn as a turkey vulture, purple finch, loon or herring gull flies past. Everyone crowds around a tree trying to catch a glimpse of a ruby-crowned kinglet, a hairy woodpecker or a magnolia warbler.

A mother deer and two feisty babies are spotted in the distance. I've never witnessed two spotted fawns leaping, hopping and racing back and forth quite like this. It almost looked like two dogs chasing each other about the large field. One of the youngsters in our group pleaded with his dad to leave the bird walk so he could get a better look at the deer. Birds were a much more difficult target to see for this seven year old.

Each bird family needs a certain area around its nest to provide it with the necessary food it needs. Once established with a nest and a mate, for the most part it stops singing, so by August the noisy atmosphere is quieter. My favourite song is the song of the white-throated sparrow. When I hear that call, I think of Algonquin. Especially in early summer this distinctive whistle is hard to miss or be confused with any other call.

Certain birds like the raven are a common sight year round. With its large beak, noisy call and long tail feathers, it is easy to tell the difference between it and a crow. The crow flies south while the raven stays in the park all winter.

All eyes turn as three loons fly in the distance. Sean asks us to notice the large legs dangling out from behind as they fly. Loons have great difficulty walking on land. They need a very long strip of water to take off. Sometimes after a rain, the water-covered highway looks like a stream and if a loon gets confused, it will land on the highway and not be able to get off. Many loons will die on land because of their inability to get airborne again. Loons have four or so different calls and at night they can be heard lamenting from afar.

264

Since the loon does so badly on land its nests are made on the ground close to shore so it can slide from its nest directly into the water. This makes its nests quite vulnerable to being destroyed by humans and their boats. Our highly industrialized North American Society smelt ores and burn coal and oil in enormous quantities. The smoke and gases like sulphur and nitrogen dioxide pollutants come to the earth in acid rain and snow and cause our lakes to become acidic.

Some experts predict that by the end of the century, over 48,000 lakes in Ontario will become dead because of acidification including most of the lakes in Algonquin Park. I don't have to tell you what that would mean to the birds, and other wildlife dependent on life in the lakes. It would be sad to be in Algonquin and not hear the echoing ringing laughter of the loon.

We saw some yellow warblers shyly hiding out in some bush, a few hawks making lazy circles in the sky and even heard the rat a tat tat of a Yellow-bellied Sapsucker. This woodpecker drills regular rows of holes in the bark of many trees and then returns to drink the sap that flows from the wounds and to eat the insects attracted to the sap. As a result many trees are weakened and this leads to their premature death.

One has to be quick to catch a glimpse of the Ruby-throated Hummingbird darting from place to place. These hummingbirds depend on the nectar from flowers but supplement their diet with tiny insects and sometimes the sap oozing from the holes drilled by Sapsuckers. Imagine this teeny weenie bird flying thousands of miles to Central America to avoid starvation.

Another one of my favourite birds is the Cedar Waxwing. It is an elegant looking bird with a pointed crown, silky velvety coat and red wax-like tips on some of its wing feathers. It nests late in July or early August so it can raise its young when the berry supply is at it's peak. We got to see them flying around the bushes where the chokeberries were in abundance.

If the birds are all hidden away and we can't sight any, then we all start "pishing". It's not what you think. We don't urinate communally. "Pishing" is a birdwatcher's term for making sounds that replicate the distress call of birds. Other birds hearing this sound are drawn into the area to take a look as a way of scouting out danger. By making this pishing sound, birds become more visible.

It's nice to start the morning training your eyes and ears to be more acute. Patience is a virtue and a must for birding. Another must is a good pair of binoculars and a birding book that can be purchased at the Park Museum. "You can't tell who the players are without a program." The nice thing about being with other people is the enthusiasm that different visitors bring to this sport.

People keep lists of their citings and compare notes about where and when they saw various species. With many eyes and ears focused, the chance of picking up signals is improved. Sean is an excellent guide and knows many of the different calls and songs. He can often tell which bird it is just by the way it flies or lands. Occasionally he brings a tape recorder and lets us listen to a tape of different birdcalls to familiarize ourselves.

I become very frustrated when I hear that some species of birds are becoming less in number. Some think it is because of increasing pollution, the disappearance of their winter home, the tropical rainforests in South America, or the continued use of D.D.T. in South America that is responsible. Birds are sensitive forecasters of what is happening to our environment. Natural habitats and wildlife are being exterminated.

Noah sent a dove out from the ark to see if there was dry

land available to live on after the destruction of the world by the Flood. Our biblical messengers are telling us that our environment is in danger. It's time to stop the destruction of our rainforests, the use of dangerous pesticides and the acid rain that is killing our lakes.

Buy binoculars, a birding book, and head out to your nearest park. If you want a real treat, head up to Algonquin Park and go on a bird walk with one of the naturalists. Be sure to keep your ears and eyes wide-open, start pishing and I'm sure you'll attract some birds. Don't delay, the birds may be disappearing!

HUG A TREE

While exploring a small island across from Camp Arowhon on Tepee Lake in Algonquin Park I began talking to a large pine tree that was growing close to a rocky landing beside an old much-used campfire site. The tree was about 80 years old and had been growing there since the destruction of the white pine by the loggers in the early 1900's.

The tree told me how the loggers came and annihilated its mother and father, grandparents, uncles and aunts. It was a frightening story; one of terror and cold-blooded murder. The tree had feared for its own life but somehow was spared from the axes and saws of the loggers.

The tree had seen many changes come to the tiny island. It told me about the shy deer that came to visit and the mischievous chipmunks that played in the forest nearby. It told me about the various birds that used the island for their nests and how when the newborn birds were first hatched they ran and jumped, shielded on the floor of the forest by small shrubs. Perhaps the most fascinating stories were about the people

267

who came to the island and sat under the tree seeking its shelter and protection from the wind, rain and sun.

Now, looking back, the tree was amazed that it had survived. In the winter the ground is covered with snow and there is an awesome stillness all over the frozen lake. Many storms have raged and fierce winds blew destroying much fragile vegetation all around. Many times insects have attacked.

There were times when tourists came with axes and knives and cut holes in its bark and injured it. Yet there were other times when its dead branches were lovingly trimmed by some canoeist or traveler and used for firewood. There were many campfires built and many foods eaten and enjoyed. It always marvelled at the way man could build a fire and put it out not damaging any of its surroundings.

The tree continued to talk. "My life has been rooted in this one spot for so many years. I have watched the changes of the seasons; the animals come and go; and the growth and death all around me. I am thankful that the loggers spared me when they killed my parents. I now watch my children and their off-spring grow. I am grateful for the rain and sun that nourish me as well as the wind that moves my branches. I love the silent night with the huge moon and glistening stars illuminating the expansive sky. The Northern Lights that come each summer are a special gift. I never get tired of seeing shooting stars, rainbows and butterflies."

"Every living thing has a purpose. Even after I die I hope that my wood will be used to fuel a fire or help in building some structure. I wish that you will remember me and that you will come back with your children and grandchildren to visit me and lean on my trunk and marvel at how high I have grown."

I put my arms around the old tree and hugged it. For a few minutes I was at one with its bark and its roots. I felt warmed and supported by its trunk. I shared its dream of peaceful existence. I hoped that I could come back with my great grandchildren to visit. I dreamed that the tree would never stop talking to me.

CHAPTER TWENTY-ONE
LIFE IS SHORT – EAT DESSERT FIRST

What does it take to stimulate you to take a vacation? How long do you have to work, how many hours do you have to put in, and what do you have to get accomplished before you give yourself permission to take a break?

In 1977 Bonnie and I were working quite hard and didn't feel we had permission to take another holiday. We had been away on sabbatical in 1975 and we were trying to build back our savings and establish our life again in the city. The death of three friends would change our minds and remind us of the lesson that life is just too short to work it away.

When I was a medical student, I had a mentor Dr. Tom Malcho a family doctor dedicated to helping people. He ran a very busy practice and also helped out in the community doing work with teenagers who had problems with drugs. I followed him around and watched him work always struck by his dedication and sincerity in trying to help. We worked in the medical tents of some rock festivals together.

I watched him helping teenagers who were involved with drugs. I worked with him at Rochdale Clinic treating teenagers with multiple problems and I always wanted to emulate the kind of hardworking attitude that he portrayed. In the summer of 1977, he died suddenly at the age of 30. I was shocked.

Dr. Stan Kushnir was an old friend of mine from summer camp when I was just an adolescent. I had known him and his parents ever since I was a child. While in medical school he became president of the Student Council and was quite dedicated to student affairs and trying to improve the medical school experience. After he graduated, he went into Family Practice and then became interested in hypnosis. He was fascinated by the connection between the mind and the body. He became a very experienced hypnotist and was instrumental in helping to establish the Ontario Society of Clinical Hypnosis as one of its principal organizers.

He soon found that hypnosis was such a valuable tool that he left general practice and went into full-time hypnosis. I identified very strongly with him. I was very upset when I learned in the fall of 1977 that he was killed in a motor vehicle accident. He was only 29 years old.

I spoke of Dr. Andy Wong earlier in the book. He was a classmate of mine at the University of Toronto. We interned together at the Toronto East General Hospital and when I visited him in Hong Kong, I stayed with him and his wife Luciante for two weeks. I got to know him, his family and his way of life. We spent hours talking about acupuncture and he showed me his acupuncture equipment and did some demonstrations. They were tremendously hospitable and looked after our every whim going out of their way to accommodate us and include us as part of their family. Soon after the death of the other two physicians, I got a letter from Luciante saying that Andy had died from an adeno-carcinoma of his lung at the age of 29.

Death has always been an instigator for change in my life. We have to live our lives to the fullest at the moment and not put things off for the future, because sometimes the future never comes.

After feeling the loss of these three important individuals, I took their deaths as a signal or message that it was time to take a break and end our non-stop working, with a holiday.

We had always wanted to go to Sri Lanka and had seen beautiful photographs of the island. We booked a flight via London to Sri Lanka for one month at Christmas. It was a wonderful vacation where we got back into the spirit of traveling. It brought back all the feelings and memories of our sabbatical.

The vacation enabled me to, once again, take time out from my busy schedule to look at what we had accomplished in a year and a half since our last trip. We began to think about what direction we would go in the future. We also realized that it was time to begin our family and I made some important decisions regarding the future of my medical orientation and my focus on holistic medicine.

It took the deaths of three people with whom I identified, to stimulate me to travel again. Even now when someone I love dies, I realize just how short life really is and how important it is to take advantage of every opportunity to enjoy myself.

CHAPTER TWENTY-TWO
THE TRUE MEANING OF GIVING

Most parents teach their children that when guests visit, it is important to make them feel at home, give them something to eat and make them feel welcome.

Wherever we travelled anywhere in the world the concept of hospitality was practiced by every culture and every country in every part of the world. Wherever we went, we were welcomed into people's homes, given food to eat, beds to sleep in, and had every little need taken care of. Often the hosts would expect nothing in return. They wouldn't even require us to be a certain way, to act a certain way, or to dress a certain way. We could just be ourselves and totally be looked after.

However, of all the places that we visited, there was a small village in Yugoslavia, south of the island of Raab, where we were treated to the true meaning of giving.

We were traveling in a rented car down the coast of Yugoslavia and our intention was to make our way along the Dalmatian Coast to Mount Negro. We picked up two hitch-hikers by the road. Sophia lived in a small border town south of the island of Raab and even though it was a fair distance, we decided to see if we could travel all the way from Zagreb to this town, so that we could bring Sophia back to her family. She was traveling with a boy from France, with whom she had been living for the past number of months.

When we arrived at this village in coastal Yugoslavia, we were greeted to a reception equal to the one she got. We were immediately invited to stay overnight, given a large room, and plenty of fruit to eat. We were told we could stay for as long as we wanted.

We went out for walks during the daytime to come back to fabulous lunches and suppers and the friendliness of a family atmosphere. We went picking figs, fresh off the tree and tasted the greatest Yugoslavian cooking imaginable. We were aware of the fact that these people were treating us unselfishly and without desiring anything in return. For them, giving was unconditional; that to expect something in return was not true giving.

When it came time to leave they actually seemed insulted. They made it seem like we were abandoning them. One of the next-door neighbours got up early in the morning to make us a special baklava. All the family came out to wish us goodbye. The mother even cried when she saw us leave. We truly had the feeling that we were welcomed as somebody special and that we were part of the family.

Another time, a few months later, we were traveling fairly inexpensively on the island of Tonga and were staying at one of the small spartan hotels on the island. While on the beach one day, we bumped into a man named Jack Bell who invited us back to the large hotel on the island for supper.

We had a pleasant, relaxing meal watching the sunset. We spoke to him and his wife, Dorothy, who were ardent travelers. When it came time to pay the bill, Jack treated us and told us that we were his guests and that he would be insulted if we tried to pay. He told us that the next time we picked up someone and took them out for dinner, that we should tell them that the meal is on him. In this way we would be passing on the good deed and carrying on the tradition of kindness of one traveler to another.

Years later, when we were in a better financial position, we did pick up a young couple hitchhiking in Sri Lanka and we treated them to an elegant meal. We told them that this meal was being sponsored by Jack Bell and advised them to pass on the good deed by treating some other couple to a meal on Mel Borins.

There is a true spirit of giving when traveling. Being away from home, you treat every situation, every setting and every evening as if it is your only home. People all over the world seem to share the golden rule, "do unto others as you would have them do unto you."

CHAPTER TWENTY-THREE
SPECTACLES IN THE AIRPLANE TOILET

At the beginning of our sabbatical in 1989, we were traveling on a flight from L.A. to Tahiti. As I was bending over changing my son's dirty diaper in the washroom on board the plane my eyeglasses fell out of my shirt pocket into the toilet and down into the holding tank to join all the excrements of the passengers on board.

I sheepishly went to the flight attendant and told her of my plight. Apparently I wasn't the first person to have committed this faux pas. She laughed and took me to where the rubber gloves were kept. She explained that I had to put on the gloves and stick my hand into the toilet, down the bowl, into the holding tank and search for my eyeglasses myself.

We were going on a four-month voyage and my glasses were extremely important to me. So with much hesitation I put on the glove, reached into the guck and felt around. After a few minutes, I still had not discovered anything but liquid and toilet paper. I found dipping my hand in excrement was not very enjoyable. I kept thinking of AIDS, hepatitis, and other communicable diseases. I was feeling kind of queasy, so I decided that this was a lost cause. I gave up and returned to my seat with a sense of hopelessness and defeat.

It took me a few minutes to think about the consequences of not having my glasses on this four and a half month holiday and I decided to return to the stewardess. She was more supportive this time and with a great deal of encouragement I put on a new pair of gloves, swallowed my pride and imagined how many other people had been in this predicament before me.

This time I took a different approach. I surrendered to the fear and let the universe look after the danger. After groping around more intensely this time, much to my amazement I found my glasses. I looked at them for a long time before deciding whether I was going to keep them. I started the long process of cleaning all the faeces off the frames.

The take home lesson is whenever you go to a washroom on an airplane put your eyeglasses in your pants pocket and if you are up to your wrist in faeces, don't stop searching.

Like traveling, sometimes you are faced with uncomfortable situations where you are going through something unpleasant. You feel lost, unsure, and sloshing around in manure. The lesson is don't give up, keep searching and you will re-own an extension of yourself.

CHAPTER TWENTY-FOUR

D.O.A

HOW TO AVOID DEPRESSION WHEN THE VACATION IS OVER

There is a joke about a psychiatrist who used to get sick every time he went on vacation. It seemed his illness was brought on because he felt so guilty about leaving his patients. Then he went through ten years of psychoanalysis. Now he only gets sick when he gets back home.

Coming home after a holiday is not easy. Sometimes it's a relief to have your own toilet seat, cook your own food just like you like it, and be close to your family and friends. There can be a certain excitement felt when arriving back to familiar surroundings. However often it can be quite depressing. People mourn the freedom, the novelty, the ending of the vacation dream.

I used to wear a pair of old shoes in my medical office. They were extremely comfortable and moulded to my feet. The heels were worn away on the outside and the shape of the shoes was slanted and crooked. In 1981 I left the shoes behind to travel around the world.

During the sabbatical I walked mainly on thongs or sandals and my feet adjusted by being spread out and relaxed. Not only did the way I walked change but in many ways I truly felt like a different person after being away for so long.

After returning to Toronto and my medical practice, I tried on the old shoes. But they just didn't fit any more. It was as if I was walking in someone else's footwear.

After a few months of working and getting back to my old

ways of doing things, I put on the old shoes again and lo and behold the shoes fit again perfectly. Once I got back into the old routines and patterns of behaviour, I reverted back to my former self. One of the challenges of returning home after a holiday, is to remember what we learned about the way the world can be far from our cosy home reality. How do we pre-serve our insights and self-awareness once we re-enter our rut?

IF THE VACATION WAS SO GREAT, HOW COME I FEEL DOWN?

Darren is a busy successful doctor, married with four beautiful children. He felt overwhelmed and depressed by the demands of his life. Darren rarely made time for himself and felt like he was giving so much to his family and patients, that there was nothing left for him by the end of the day. He planned a one-week vacation without the family on a Caribbean Island and felt truly liberated.

Darren slept in, read books, went for walks, marvelled at the beauty of the scenery and felt like a different person. When he arrived home all the demands and harshness of his life returned and he became depressed again. It was so severe he found himself crying inappropriately and resenting everyone in his life.

In psychotherapy with me, Darren began to focus on what he appreciated when he was away and how to bring some of the vacation into his day-to-day life. How could he read, get in touch with nature and make some alone time for himself with-out feeling guilty that he was being irresponsible to his family and job? How could he have a vacation every day of his life rather than trying to squeeze it into his time away?

Joseph was a 29 year-old psychotherapy patient of mine

who lived at home with his parents. For many years he suffered from anxiety and phobias. He worked hard in psychotherapy to face many of his fears and has been able to conquer many of them. With years of psychotherapy and self-education behind him he embarked on his first journey to a European country. He tells of his adventure:

"It all began when a mutual friend of my brother and me moved to England and invited us to come to visit. My brother was not able to go so I chose to go alone. After finalizing all the travel arrangements I noticed an unusually extreme excitable feeling. I was so keyed up about going on this trip that it was difficult to contain all the energy within me. I could not remember the last time I had felt so alive."

"Since it was my first time traveling such a distance alone, as the date got closer to my departure I was feeling quite nervous. Once I got to the airport, the nervousness began to dissipate and my adventure began. My visit was only for a week and we didn't have any pre-set schedule. We decided to be spontaneous and plan it as we went along. My trip covered Birmingham, London and Manchester. We saw Buckingham Palace, Big Ben, Piccadilly Circus, Tower of London, Windsor Castle and many more sites. I couldn't believe how much I had seen and how much more there was to visit."

With a glint in his brown eyes he continues his story, "After about three days into the trip I realized something unusual about myself. It was something I had never felt before. I noticed that I did not have any feelings of anxiety, nervousness or tension. Instead I had this sense of inner peace. As I became more aware of this feeling I thought to myself that I was finally "Home". This sense of calm stayed with me throughout the vacation and I felt no fear for my safety no matter where I went."

"For the first time, since I was away from my family, I felt independent and free to make my own decisions without any interference from them. I realized that if I could go away without being held back by my fears, then all my years of therapy with Dr. Borins had paid off. I felt like I could conquer anything I set my mind to conquer."

"When I returned to Canada I was surprised at how angry I felt. My feelings of anger were very strong and I could not understand why. With a bit of self-reflection, I realized I was angry at myself, my parents and the fact that my life back home was going 'no where'. The contrast with how I felt being away and the reality of being home was overwhelming. It took a few weeks before the anger dissipated and I began to feel calm and relaxed again. The vacation had taught me invaluable lessons about myself. I know I can be an independent person and I am sure I will travel again."

Joseph is not the only person who feels angry when a holiday is over. However, he was able to understand what the anger was all about and learned from the experience.

George a forty five year old, busy executive, who runs a very high-powered company complains that there is so much work in the office that if he goes away, he has to work overtime when he returns just to catch up for the time lost. Sometimes he feels it is just not worth it.

It is true that after being away from home you come back to a pile of mail, bills and chores that need to be done. Also things at work kept piling up and sometimes you have to deal with last week's work in addition to your regular job.

There is a tendency to overdo things when you return. Therefore it is important to follow some specific tips on how to avoid depression and overwork when you come back.

TIPS TO AVOID THE POST HOLIDAY BLUES

1. Schedule some activity before you go on vacation for the first week of your return. This activity must be something you love to do like walking in the park, going to a sports game, having a massage, or meeting with a supportive friend. In this way you have something to look forward to during your first week back.

2. Develop your photos soon after returning and put them in a book and start showing them to your friends and family. In this way you remember your holiday and the good feelings return.

3. Make arrangements to be with other travelers who understand what it is like to return after a vacation. Ask them to support you when you get into the doldrums.

4. Even though you may feel obliged, don't overwork when you first get back. Pace yourself. Most things can be done over time. There are very few emergencies. Say no to new demands without feeling guilty.

5. Begin dreaming your next vacation. Choose a date and place in your mind. Write it down and go over the steps that are necessary to make the arrangements needed to ensure you will go away again. Fantasizing about your next time off gives you something to look forward to.

6. Be gentle with yourself. Wear the clothes you wore while away. Get out any trinkets, souvenirs or reminders

282

of your holiday and keep them around to help relive the memorable feelings.

7. Phone or write someone whom you met on your travels. They should understand what you are going through and help you endure the grief.

Take some preventive measures before you go away which will ensure you don't get sick or depressed when you arrive back from a holiday. Often it can be a relief to arrive home safely. Your diary, photos, souvenirs, friends made, and the images in your head help to make the transition back easier. Don't let the fear of coming home prevent you from going away.

THE BEGINNING

B y now you have no doubt come to the conclusion that I love to travel. Perhaps by reading this book some of my enthusiasm has rubbed off and vacations are more prominent in your thoughts. Since it is not easy to send everyone a postcard when away traveling, this book is my letter to tell you about what a great trip this has been.

It takes a lot of time to dream, plan, and make the space to actually go away. The dreaming stage includes visualizing and thinking about your next holiday. It begins by asking yourself- "when can I make time for a holiday?" Then put the date on your calendar, right away. If your next holiday is so far away that you do not have the calendar yet, then begin telling people you are going away in the that year, no matter how far away it is. This helps secure it in the unconscious calendar in your brain.

After the dreaming stage, comes the process of making plans and arrangements. This includes booking off the time, researching the trip and looking after the details. If you wish to travel with others, then it requires coordination to organize things so everyone can go away together. You have to arrange for flights, accommodation, travel insurance, changing money and getting visas. You may wish to read books and visit websites of places you will be visiting. Many people love the excitement of planning and enjoy the creative aspects of organizing the future.

Then comes the packing stage, when you accumulate all the things you will need to have when you are away from home. Tying up loose ends before you leave is very important: Like watering the plants, giving away the animals, and saying

JUST FOR THE HEALTH OF IT

goodbye to friends and relatives. You have to make sure that deadlines will be met, bank accounts are stable, bills coming due will be paid ahead of time and your home will be looked after. Some people think that the process of leaving is the most challenging part of the vacation.

Then comes the "getting there" or 'The Journey'. Children keep asking, "Are we there yet?" Getting there is half the fun. The process is just as important as the endpoint. Finally, you arrive at your destination. Then it is time to plan your next holiday. This book is my prescription for a healthier life and a happy holiday.

Please, **go away** without delay. Pick up the phone and book a reservation – **just for the health of it!**

'Happy trails to you'.

TRAVELLIN' MAN

Where I lay my weary head,
And make my lonely bed,
Makes no difference to me.
I was born to roam,
I've never known a home,
I just keep a traveling on.

From the moment I was born,
From the womb I was torn,
To travel around with no end.
I live on the run,
Following the sun,
Never knowing where I'll lay my head.

Tomorrow at the break of day,
I'll set on my weary way,
Singing as I travel along .
Don't you cry over me,
I love to be free,
And I wouldn't have it any other way.

Are you stuck in a rut,
Getting itchy feet,
Taste the smell of freedom everywhere.
Follow your bliss,
Give your house a goodbye kiss,
Hit the road and saddle up your horse.

.

ACKNOWLEDGEMENTS

I would like to thank my wife Bonnie, my best partner in travel, for sharing her time with me in so many far away places. I would like to acknowledge my children Larry, David and Marc for their support and tolerance during the years I spent writing this book. You are my favourite traveling companions in the world and my best excuse for taking time off.

My in-laws are inspirational models of people who love to travel. Their positive attitude and generosity enabled us to travel so much. My parents were responsible for taking me out to the country each summer when I was small and taking me away for vacations during my early growing years. Their love sowed the seeds of my vagabond spirit.

Thanks to Jerry Steinberg, Karen Fabian, Ethel Gordon, Cheri Szereszewski, Zel Goodbaum and Dan Couvrette who read the manuscript and made corrections and useful suggestions. Rita Shaughnessy at the University of Toronto helped me research this book.

I would like to acknowledge Jack McClelland, Frances Hanna, Jack David and Ian Burgham who encouraged me at different stages of this project.

My sincere thanks go to Stan Solomon and Donalee Moulton who helped edit parts of the book. John Lee did a remarkable job of designing this book.

A special thanks to all those who let me share their traveling stories.

Bon voyage

GO AWAY

ORDER FORM

I WOULD LIKE TO ORDER COPIES OF DR. BORINS BOOKS AND SONGS

PLEASE SEND ME _____ COPIES OF "GO AWAY"@ $19.95 each

$_____

plus shipping ($5.00 for first book, $3.00 for each additional book)

$_____

I enclose $_____total

PLEASE SEND ME_____ COPIES OF "AN APPLE A DAY-A HOLISTIC HEALTH PRIMER" by Mel Borins @$12.95 each

$_____

plus shipping ($5.00 for first book, $3.00 for each additional book)

$_____

I enclose $_____total

PLEASE SEND ME _____COPIES OF "SONGS OF HEALING" by Mel Borins @$19.99 each CD) ($12.99 each tape)

$_____

plus shipping ($5.00 for first CD or tape, $2.00 for each additional one)

I enclose $_____total

Mail this form along with your cheque or money order, name and address to:

Wholistic Press
Suite 405
27 Roncesvalles Ave.
Toronto, Ontario Canada
M6R 3B2   **288**